**100% NEW**

# DEVELOPING LITERACY

**Photocopiable teaching resources f**

# UNDERSTANDING AND RESPONDING TO TEXTS

## Ages 9–10

**Christine Moorcroft**

A & C Black • London

Published 2008 by A & C Black Publishers Limited
38 Soho Square, London W1D 3HB
www.acblack.com

ISBN 978-0-7136-8464-3

Copyright text © Christine Moorcroft 2008
Copyright illustrations © Bill Houston/Beehive Illustration 2008
Copyright cover illustration © Piers Baker 2008
Editor: Dodi Beardshaw
Designed by Susan McIntyre

The authors and publishers would like to thank Ray Barker and Rifat Siddiqui for their advice in producing this series of books.

The authors and publishers are grateful for permission to reproduce the following:

p.14: From 'A Martian Comes to Stay' by Penelope Lively, from *Uninvited Ghosts* by Penelope Lively. Reproduced by permission of Egmont UK. p.16: From *Bill's New Frock* by Anne Fine. Reproduced by permission of Egmont UK. From 'Bad News Bear' by Anne Fine, from *How To Write Really Badly* by Anne Fine. Reproduced by permission of Egmont UK. p.23: From *Parvana's Journey* by Deborah Ellis. Reproduced by permission of Oxford University Press. p.53: 'Early Country Village Morning' and 'Sea Timeless Song' by Grace Nichols. Reproduced by permission of Curtis Brown Group Ltd. p.55: 'Taking my pen for a walk' by Julie O'Callaghan. Reproduced by permission of the author. p.59: 'The Listeners' by Walter de la Mare. Reproduced by permission of the Literary Trustees of Walter de la Mare and the Society of Authors. Every effort has been made to trace copyright holders and to obtain their permission for use of copyright material. The authors and publishers would be pleased to rectify any error or omission in future editions.

A CIP catalogue record for this book is available from the British Library.

Printed by Halstan Printing Group, Amersham, Buckinghamshire.

A&C Black uses paper produced with elemental chlorine-free pulp, harvested from managed sustainable forests.

# Contents

# Non-fiction

## Instructions

| | |
|---|---|
| **Hot Potatoes user** | record the process of finding out how to use new software |
| **Helpdesk** | write answers to questions about using new software |
| **Hot Potatoes glossary** | distinguish between everyday use of words and their subject-specific use |

## Recounts

| | |
|---|---|
| **Interview** | devise questions to find the facts of an event in order to plan and write a recount |
| **The interviewer** | plan an interview with a visitor to the school |
| **The best questions** | develop the children's awareness of the types of questions that elicit the most information |
| **Recount chronology: 1** | identify how a recount information text is structured |
| **Recount chronology: 2** | identify how a recount information text is structured |
| **Recount features** | identify the key features of a recount |

## Persuasive writing

| | |
|---|---|
| **Dear Editor: 1** | identify the devices used in letters to persuade readers to do something or to agree with a point of view |
| **Dear Editor: 2** | identify the devices used in letters to persuade readers to do something or to agree with a point of view |
| **Persuasive language** | identify the devices used in letters to persuade readers to do something or to agree with a point of view |
| **A different bias: 1** | infer writers' perspectives from what is written and from what is implied |
| **A different bias: 2** | infer writers' perspectives from what is written and from what is implied |

# Poetry

## Poetic style

| | |
|---|---|
| **Robert Louis Stevenson** | infer writers' perspectives from what is written and from what is implied |
| **Grace Nichols** | infer writers' perspectives from what is written and from what is implied |
| **Researching a poet** | identify key aspects of a poet's style |
| **Free verse: 1** | develop understanding of free verse |
| **Free verse: 2** | develop understanding of free verse |

## Classic narrative poems

| | |
|---|---|
| **Is there anybody there?** | compare the usefulness of techniques such as visualisation, prediction and empathy in exploring the meaning of texts |
| **The traveller** | compare the usefulness of techniques such as visualisation, prediction and empathy in exploring the meaning of texts |
| **The Listeners** | explore how writers use language for dramatic effects |
| **The Listeners atmosphere** | identify the words that create the atmosphere in a poem |

## Choral and performance

| | |
|---|---|
| **Listening to poems** | record responses to poems they listen to |
| **Read it aloud** | read a poem they have not listened to and discuss the best ways of reading it aloud |
| **Sounds good** | identify the words, phrases and poetic devices that help to create the atmosphere in a poem |
| **Sounds good to me** | record responses to the poems they most like listening to |

# Introduction

0% New Developing Literacy Understanding and Responding Texts is a series of seven photocopiable activity books for veloping children's responses to different types of text and ir understanding of the structure and purposes of different pes of texts.

e books provide learning activities to support strands 7 and 8 the literacy objectives of the Primary Framework for Literacy: derstanding and interpreting texts and Engaging with and sponding to texts.

e structure of 100% New Developing Literacy Understanding d Responding to Texts: Ages 9–10 is designed to complement e objectives of the Primary Framework and include the range of xt types suggested in the planning for Year 5.

0% New Developing Literacy Understanding and Responding Texts: Ages 9–10 addresses the following learning objectives m the Primary Framework for Literacy:

Understanding and interpreting texts

Making notes on, and using evidence from across a text to explain events or ideas

Inferring writers' perspectives from what is written and from what is implied

Comparing different types of narrative and information texts and identifying how they are structured

Distinguishing between everyday use of words and their subject-specific use

Exploring how writers use language for comic and dramatic effects.

Engaging with and responding to texts

Reflecting on reading habits and preferences and planning personal reading goals

Comparing the usefulness of techniques such as visualisation, prediction and empathy in exploring the meaning of texts

Comparing how a common theme is presented in poetry, prose and other media.

e structure of 100% New Developing Literacy Understanding d Responding to Texts: Ages 9–10 focuses on the following pes of text:

Narrative (novels and stories by significant children's authors, traditional stories, myths and legends, stories from other cultures, older literature, film narrative, dramatic conventions)

Non-fiction (instructions, recounts, information texts, persuasive writing)

Poetry (poetic style, classic narrative poems, choral and performance).

## The activities

Some of activities can be carried out with the whole class, some are more suitable for small groups and others are for individual work. It is important that the children are encouraged to enjoy novels, stories, plays, films and poetry – not just to learn about how they are written – and that they have opportunities to listen to, repeat, learn, recite and join in poems for enjoyment. Many of the activities can be adapted for use at different levels, to suit the differing levels of attainment of the children; several can be used in different ways as explained in the notes which follow.

## Reading

Most children will be able to carry out the activities independently but a few might need help in reading some of the instructions on the sheets. It is expected that someone will read them to or with them, or explain them, if necessary.

## Organisation

The activities require very few resources besides pencils, crayons, scissors and glue. Other materials are specified in the Teachers' notes on the pages: for example, fiction, poetry or information books, websites and CD-ROMs.

## Extension activities

Most of the activity sheets end with a challenge (Now try this!) which reinforces and extends the children's learning. These more challenging activities might be appropriate for only a few children; it is not expected that the whole class should complete them, although many more children might benefit from them with appropriate assistance – possibly as a guided or shared activity. On some pages there is space for the children to complete the extension activities, but others will require a notebook or a separate sheet of paper.

## Accompanying CD

The enclosed CD-ROM contains all the activity sheets from the book and allows you to edit them for printing or saving. This means that modifications can be made to differentiate the activities further to suit individual pupils' needs. See page 13 for more details.

# Notes on the activities

The notes below expand upon those which are provided at the bottom of most activity pages. They give ideas and suggestions for making the most of the activity sheet, including suggestions for the whole-class introduction, the plenary session or for follow-up work using an adapted version of the activity sheet. To help teachers to select appropriate learning experiences for their pupils, the activities are grouped into sections within each book but the pages need not be presented in the order in which they appear, unless otherwise stated.

## Stories and poems featured or suggested in this book and supplementary texts

Novels and stories by significant children's authors
Penelope Lively: *A Martian Comes To Stay*, *The Ghost of Thomas Kempe*
Other children's stories by Penelope Lively: *Astercote*, *The Whispering Knights*, *The Wild Hunt of Hagworthy*, *The Driftway*, *The House in Norham Gardens*, *Going Back*, *A Stitch in Time*, *The Revenge of Samuel Stokes*, *The Stained Glass Window*, *1976*, *Boy Without a Name*, *Fanny's Sister*, *Fanny and the Monsters*, *Fanny and the Battle of Potter's Piece*, *Dragon Trouble*, *Debbie and the Little Devil*, *A House Inside Out*, *Princess by Mistake*, *Judy and the Martian*, *The Cat, the Crow and the Banyan Tree*, *Good Night, Sleep Tight*, *Two Bears and Joe*, *Staying with Grandpa*, *Lost Dog*, *One, Two, Three … Jump*

Anne Fine: *Bill's New Frock* (Mammoth), *How To Write Really Badly* (Mammoth)
Other children's stories by Anne Fine: *The Summer House Loon*, *The Other Darker Ned*, *The Stone Menagerie*, *Round Behind the Ice-house*, *The Granny Project*, *Scaredy-Cat*, *Anneli the Art Hater*, *Madame Doubtfire*, *A Pack of Liars*, *Crummy Mummy and Me*, *Goggle-Eyes*, *The Country Pancake*, *Stranger Danger?*, *The Worst Child I Ever Had*, *The Book of the Banshee*, *Design a Pram*, *The Same Old Story Every Year*, *The Haunting of Pip Parker*, *The Angel of Nitshill Road*, *The Chicken Gave It To Me*, *Flour Babies*, *Press Play*, *Step by Wicked Step*, *Countdown*, *Jennifer's Diary*, *The Tulip Touch*, *Loudmouth Louis*, *Roll Over Roly*, *Charm School*, *Bad Dreams*, *Notso Hotso*, *How to Cross the Road and Not Turn Into a Pizza*, *Up on Cloud Nine*, *The More the Merrier*, *Frozen Billy*, *The True Story of Christmas*, *Raking the Ashes*, *It Moved!*, *On the Summer-House Steps*, *The Road of Bones*, *Jamie and Angus Together*, *Ivan the Terrible*, *Saving Miss Mirabelle*

Traditional stories, fables, myths, legends
*The Golden Hoard – Myths and Legends of the World* (Geraldine McCaughrean, Orion); *The Silver Treasure – Myths and Legends of the World* (Geraldine McCaughrean, Orion); *Storm Boy* (Paul Lewis, Barefoot); *Tales from the Old World* (Kevin Crossley-Holland, Dolphin); *Aesop's Fables* (Geraldine McCaughrean, Pelican); *The Lion and the Rat Fables of La Fontaine* (Brian Wildsmith, OUP); *Arthur: The Seeing Stone* (Kevin Crossley-Holland, Orion); *Orchard Book of Greek Myths* (Geraldine McCaughrean, Orchard); *Arion and the Dolphin* (Vikram Seth, Orion); *How the World Began* (Andrew Matthews, Macdonald); *The Orchard Book of Creation Myths* (Margaret Mayo, Orchard);

Stories from other cultures
*Parvana's Journey* (Deborah Ellis, OUP); *On the Run* (Elizabeth Laird, Mammoth); *Abdullah's Butterfly* (Janine M Fraser, HarperCollins); *Grace and Family* (Mary Hoffman, Frances Lincoln); *Tales from Africa* (Mary Medlicott, Kingfisher); *The Barefoot Book of Animal Tales* (Naomi Adler, Barefoot); *Stories from a Shona Childhood* (Charles Mungoshi, Baobab Books); *The Well* (Mildred Taylor, Heinemann); *Black Poetry* (compiled b[y] Grace Nicholls, Blackie); *Zlata's Diary* (Zlata Filipoviv, Puffin); *Seasons of Splendour, Tales and Myths of Ancient India* (Madh[u] Jaffrey, Puffin); *Chasing The Sun, Stories from Africa* (edited by Veronique Tadjo)

Older literature
The *Just William* series of stories (Richmal Crompton, Macmillan); *The Secret Garden* (Frances Hodgson Burnett, Puffin); *Tom's Midnight Garden* (Philippa Pearce, Puffin); *The Borrowers* (Mary Norton, Puffin); *The Jungle Book* (Rudyard Kipling, OUP); *The Railway Children* (Edith Nesbit, Penguin); *Black Beauty* (Anna Sewell, Penguin)

Useful books of poems
*The Works* (chosen by Paul Cookson, Macmillan); *I Like This Poem* (chosen by Kaye Webb, Puffin); *The Hutchinson Treasury of Children's Poetry* (edited by Alison Sage, Hutchinson); *The Kingfisher Book of Children's Poetry* (selected by Michael Rosen Kingfisher); *The Puffin Book of Twentieth-Century Children's Verse* (edited by Brian Patten, Puffin); *The Poetry Book: Poems for Children* (chosen by Fiona Waters, Dolphin); *Read Me: A Poem A Day For The National Year Of Reading* (chosen by Gab[y] Morgan, Macmillan); *Classic Poems to Read Aloud* (selected by James Berry, Kingfisher); *The Oxford Treasury of Classic Poems* (OUP); *A Child's Garden of Verses* and *Underwoods* (Robert Louis Stevenson, (first published 1885) Simon & Schuster); *Give Yourself a Hug* (Grace Nichols, A & C Black); *Asana and the Animals: A Book of Pet Poems*, (Grace Nichols, Walker Books); *Paint Me A Poem: New Poems Inspired by Art in the Tate* (Justine Rowden, A & C Black)

Useful collections of stories
*The Puffin Book of Stories for nine-year-olds* (ed Wendy Cooling Puffin); *I Like This Story, A taste of fifty favourites* (Kaye Webb, Puffin)

Useful websites
Narrative
Penelope Lively's official website http://penelopelively.net/
Anne Fine's official website http://www.annefine.co.uk/
Deborah Ellis http://www.allenandunwin.com/Authors/apEllis.asp

Beddgelert: the village and the origin of the legend
http://www.snowdonia.org/
http://www.data-wales.co.uk/beddgelert.htm
http://www.beddgelerttourism.com/index_main.htm
http://www.bbc.co.uk/wales/northwest/sites/history/pages/bedd gelert.shtml

ıst William series http://www.sharpsoftware.co.uk/william/
tp://www.fantasticfiction.co.uk/c/richmal-crompton/

yths, fables, legends
tp://home.freeuk.net/elloughton13/theatre.htm
tp://www.mysteriousbritain.co.uk/legends/legendstemplate.html
egends of Britain)
tp://www.aesopfables.com/ (Fables of Aesop)

lm
ww.bfi.org.uk/education/teaching/primary.html
ww.britfilms.tv
ww.bbcmotiongallery.com
ww.britishpathe.com
ww.video.google.co.uk

ual-language books
tp://www.kingston.gov.uk/browse/leisure/libraries/childrens_library
service/dual_language.htm

he Piano by Aidan Gibbons: for links using IWB software see
e Primary Strategy. The following work without IWB software:
tp://www.gutenberg.org/dirs/etext99/rlwyc10.txt
tp://video.google.com/videoplay?docid=5422822544003533526

on-fiction
ttp://news.bbc.co.uk/cbbcnews/hi/uk/default.stm (a news site
or children)

oetry
Warning' by Jenny Joseph
tp://www.wheniamanoldwoman.com/pages/348544/index.htm
about the poem)
oetry to listen to http://laurable.com/audio.html
tp://www.poets.org/audio.php
ttp://www.bbc.co.uk/arts/poetry/outloud/

tobert Louis Stevenson
ttp://www.nls.uk/rlstevenson/ (biography and links to other sites)
ttp://www.poetryloverspage.com/poets/stevenson/stevenson_ind.
tml
ttp://www.bartleby.com/people/StvnsnR.html
ttp://www.poetryloverspage.com/poets/stevenson/collections/
hilds_garden_of_verses.html (poems online)

irace Nichols
ttp://www.contemporarywriters.com/authors/?p=auth79
biographical and other details)

his book is divided into three main sections: Narrative, Non-
ction and Poetry. These are sub-divided to match the Planning
Jnits of the Primary Framework for Literacy.

# Narrative

## Novels and stories by significant children's authors

The activities in this section are about stories by contemporary children's writers, with a focus on Penelope Lively and Anne Fine. Other authors to read include Joan Aiken, David Almond, Malorie Blackman, Judy Blume, Betsy Byars, Helen Cresswell, Gillian Cross, Berlie Doherty, Michael Foreman, Kevin Crossley-Holland, Dick King-Smith, Michelle Magorian, Margaret Mahy, Michael Morpurgo, Beverley Naidoo, Terry Pratchett, Philip Pullman, J K Rowling, Robert Westall and Jacqueline Wilson.

**A Martian comes to stay** and **Stories by Penelope Lively** (pages 14–15) provide an opportunity to introduce an author through a short story and to encourage the children to read her other work. The children might see the humour in the matter-of-fact response of Peter and his gran to a Martian knocking at the front door and in the everyday language Gran uses to talk about him: 'Should have offered him a cup of tea. He'll have had a fair journey.' You could draw out that, unlike in some children's stories (for example, *Come Away From the Water Shirley* by John Burningham and *Andrew's Bath* by David McPhail) the adult believes the improbable-sounding messages from the child rather than just humouring him or her. Draw the children's attention to the real-life setting and the relationship between the realistic characters in this setting and a fantastical character. This then can be found in other stories by Penelope Lively: for instance *The Ghost of Thomas Kempe*.

**Anne Fine story openings** and **Story openings** (pages 16–17) can be used to introduce the author by encouraging the children to talk about other stories they have read by Anne Fine. The focus here is on openings. Compare them with the openings of other stories in which the setting is described in detail before any action begins and note that in these two stories Anne Fine starts the action immediately – the reader is drawn into the story right away. Discuss other ways in which the author uses the opening: to introduce the main character and to present the problem he faces. The character's name is introduced very early and the problem or issue is introduced immediately. Unlike the characters, the setting is not described directly. The children could notice whether other story openings by Anne Fine have these similarities. They could also notice whether most of her stories are written in the first person or the third person or there is a balanced mixture.

## Traditional stories, myths, fables, legends

This section helps the children to distinguish between different types of traditional story and to notice the key features of each type. The children develop an awareness of how some traditional stories develop.

**Story sorts** (page 18) introduces the different types of traditional stories. Answers: *The Three Little Pigs*, *The Gingerbread Man*, *Goldilocks and the Three Bears* (fairytales – old stories that tell of enchantments or unreal incidents that could never really happen, such as bears that live in a house and talk); *The Ant and the Grasshopper*, *The Lion and the Mouse*, *The Hare and the Tortoise*, *The Fox and the Hen* (fables – stories told to teach or give a message about life); *Persephone and the Pomegranate Seeds*, *King Midas*, *The Story of Rama and Sita*, *Jason and the Golden Fleece*, *The Minotaur*, *Saint George and the Dragon* (myths – stories that are entirely or mainly fictitious and explain a phenomenon that is not understood or explain a popular belief or religious belief); *Androcles and the Lion*, *Robin Hood and the Sheriff of Nottingham*, *King Arthur and the Knights of the Round Table*, *The Story of the Glastonbury Thorn*, *King Alfred and the Cakes* (legends – stories about real people or people who are thought by some to have been real, stories that are popularly believed to be historical).

**Creation myths** (page 19) provides an opportunity to explore how a common theme (the creation of the universe) is presented in different stories. Ask the children why they think most religions have creation myths and draw out that many myths develop in order to explain things people do not understand. Some people accept these stories as history but others, including those who belong to that faith group, recognise them as traditional stories to explain the creation (something that even now is not completely understood by scientists). If they have read Rudyard Kipling's *Just-So stories*, they might be able to find similarities between these and myths.

**Fabulous fables** (page 20) focuses on the messages and teaching of Aesop's fables. For a less challenging activity you could supply the messages for the children to match to the fables: it is sensible to save while you have plenty, a liar is not believed for long, do not let flattery affect your common sense, there is strength in numbers.

**The legend of Gelert: 1** and **2** (pages 21–22) provides an opportunity to enjoy and then research a legend. You could read the story to the children or display it on an interactive whiteboard for them to follow while you read it. Stop at the part where Gelert does not greet his master when he comes home (mask the rest of the story). Ask the children why the hound does not come – what might have happened? Stop again at the part where Llewellyn finds him, and ask what they think has happened. Ask them what they would do if they were Llewellyn. Read on and, at the end, let the children talk about how the story makes them feel (it usually leaves several children in any class in tears). You could ask them later what makes the story especially sad. They could also note down the facts of the story as if researching a news report. Ask them to write up their notes in sentences and read them aloud. Is this as sad as the story? Discuss the differences between the different types of text – fact and fiction. Using books, CD-ROMs and the Internet, the children should be able to find out more about Llewellyn, when and where he lived and any other historical facts and about the village of Beddgelert and how the legend is thought to have arisen (see the list of sources on page 6).

## Stories from other cultures

These activities develop the children's awareness of the ways in which culture affects the behaviour of and interactions and relationships between characters in a story. They also explore authors' use of language, particularly literal and figurative language for descriptions and for creating an effect. The activities can be linked with work in citizenship or living in a diverse world and on children's rights – human rights.

***Parvana's Journey*** and **Language in *Parvana's Journey*** (pages 23–24) focus on the way in which the author, Deborah Ellis, uses language to highlight the desperate situation of Parvana, Hassan (the baby she found in a bombed house) and Asif (the boy she discovered living in a cave). The children also become aware of how the culture in which these children live affects their behaviour, their relationships, how they interact with other people and how the different adults they meet respond to them. Parvana's family became split up during the bombing of Kabul during the war in Afghanistan. Her father, who was with her, died and her main aim is to find her mother and other surviving members of her family. You could focus on the techniques the author uses to communicate the dangers and the immense difficulties Parvana faces: narrative about Parvana's thoughts (for example, 'But now she could only think about her empty belly'), literal language that says precisely what she does ('She sighed deeply') and letters to a friend in which she describes a wonderful place that she imagines.
Parvana's imagined Green Valley is used as a comparison/contrast with her real life throughout the chapter in order to highlight Parvana's plight in the Hidden Valley. The Green Valley is 'full of food' but Parvana is starving. In the Green Valley she 'ate an orange as big as my head and three bowls of strawberry ice cream'/'no one in Afghnistan has ice cream any more'. In the Green Valley 'We can drink the water without boiling it, and we don't get sick' suggests that in real life they have to boil water before they can drink it and that it can make them ill. 'All the children here have both arms and legs' describes what you would expect children to have but shows that Parvana is used to seeing children with arms or legs missing: 'Maybe Asif's leg will even grow back'. The children should notice the way in which the author chooses words to create and effect. They should notice adjectives. Note also the comparisons: *so bright that*, *as big as my head*, *like we are celebrating the end of Ramadan*, and the strong verbs: *hurt, sighed, celebrating, love*.

**Characters and culture** (page 25) presents a picture of the setting faced by the children in *Parvana's Journey* (and by many real children in war zones). What would the children do if they stepped into this picture? Ask them to think about what they would want to do, whether this would be possible, and how – and, if not, what might they do instead.

**Culture and actions** (page 26) focuses on the ways in which story characters' responses to situations are affected by their culture. The children could use copies of this page to record eir observations on Parvana, Asif and Hassan in *Parvana's urney* and on the actions of characters in other books set in a nge of cultures. Ask them to imagine the same events ppening to people in other cultures and to consider whether ey would respond in the same ways, and why.

## lder literature

hese activities introduce older children's stories and provide a ormat for a focused reading journal. They also develop the hildren's awareness of the differences of relationships, customs nd attitudes with those in their own experience and help them o identify language registers that differ from contemporary ones.

 older novel (page 27) provides a reading journal format in hich the children can record the main events of a book they ad or listen to in serial form. It helps them to record the main ents of a chapter, anything that puzzles them or questions they ant to ask about it, and their predictions about what might ppen. During plenary sessions they could tell the others their estions; encourage the others to suggest answers based on at they know of the story, the setting and the characters. They uld also talk about their predictions and give reasons. courage the others to question these and give reasons.

fferent dialogue (page 28) presents a passage from a story itten in the 1950s. It invites the children to compare the language William and his friends with the language *they* use when talking *their* friends. They might notice the apostrophes used to denote issing letters – a device used to communicate the way in which e boys speak. The main differences between this dialogue and odern children's dialogue are the popular words and cclamations: *gosh, as near as near, get one quite, jolly good*. Ask e children what they might say instead. They could also enact e scene using the type of language they normally use.

rmal or informal (page 29) provides a passage from a ildren's novel from 1911 (*The Secret Garden* by Frances odgson-Burnett). After Mary's parents died in India she was ent to live with an uncle in England. She has found a locked arden and wants some gardening tools so that she can weed nd plant it. Martha, the maid, writes a letter to her brother to sk him if he can help. This activity draws attention to the rmality of the language used in a letter from Martha, the maid, her brother, both in addressing her brother and writing about ary ('Miss Mary').

## ilm narrative

This section focuses on the role played by the camera in elling a story, in particular a story told through 'flashbacks' nd the way in which a story can be told and emotions ommunicated without any spoken dialogue. It is based on the hort (2 minutes) animated film *The Piano* by Aidan Gibbons, which the Primary Strategy recommends for this purpose.

**The Piano: scenes** (page 30) helps the children to discuss their responses to the film *The Piano* by Aidan Gibbons. It provides a series of cards depicting scenes from the film which can be used as prompts to help the children to focus on a particular scene and what it says. After showing the film you could ask the children to put the cards in the order in which they are shown in the film and use them as prompts to help them to tell the story, using a flashback. They could also put them in the order in which they happened and compare this with the order in which they appear in the film. They could write a summary or heading for each scene. These cards can be used in conjunction with page 31.

**The Piano: mood cards** (page 31) focuses on the mood and atmosphere of *The Piano*. It also makes the children aware that a story can be told visually without words. Ask them which mood cards they used the most often. Ask them what, in each scene, gave it a particular mood or atmosphere. They could observe one another miming some of these scenes and notice how they use the posture and movements of their bodies and their facial expressions to express a feeling.

**The Piano: a life in a tune** (page 32) suggests some questions to ask the piano player in the film. The answers can be inferred from scenes in the film. During the plenary session ask the children to explain their answers and to give evidence from the film. They could also pose some questions of their own and discuss what the answers might be, and why.

**The Piano: thoughts and words** (page 33) widens the children's understanding of the characters in the film through dramatic techniques as they focus on specific scenes from the film *The Piano* and write the words the characters might say if there were dialogue. Children could 'hotseat' the pianist, to help them think in role, and also do paired role-play to establish the thoughts and words of the characters. As a further extension they could write a monologue (in the first person) for the piano player. They could also write biography of the piano player from the point of view of another character.

## Dramatic conventions

These activities combine narrative with non-fiction. It develops the children's awareness that non-fiction as well as fiction has scripts. The children learn about the differences between scripts written for broadcasts with different purposes.

**Script match** (page 34) develops the children's understanding of what is meant by a script and that television broadcasts that are not fiction can be based on a prepared script (also that some are unscripted but that the spoken words can be recorded afterwards as a transcript). When matching the scripts to the broadcasts they should consider subject language and style of language as well as person and tense.

**In the script** (page 35) develops the children's understanding of the different types and purposes of scripted television broadcasts. Before the activity it is necessary to record different types of television broadcast for the children to watch. After they have completed the activity they could watch the extracts again and notice the different techniques used: one voice or more, sounds such as music or singing, visual effects such as animation, small plays (as in advertisements), panoramic views and so on, and notice the effects of these techniques. Many programmes, e.g. chat shows, cooking programmes, sports commentaries, have unscripted as well as scripted parts. The introductions and endings will almost always be scripted.

**Presentation** (page 36) helps the children to identify the aural and visual presentation techniques used in non-fiction television and radio broadcasts and to consider the responses they evoke in an audience. They could group the broadcasts according to similarities and identify these in other broadcasts they watch. Ask them about the similarities between non-fiction television scripts and playscripts; they should consider what the director needs to know about what is to be shown on screen and what is to be heard and how these are co-ordinated.

**Evaluate a broadcast** (page 37) develops the children's skills in evaluating a television broadcast against a set of criteria. It could be adapted for use with a radio broadcast by omitting colour and camera angle. The children should consider how effective different features were (and what made them so): music, spoken words, other sounds, colour and camera angle (for example, close-ups, panoramic views, eye-level, high or low views.

# Non-fiction

## Instructions

> This section develops the children's understanding of how and where support and instructions can be found for specific purposes, including how to use and run a helpdesk and online instructions. It features activities based on the freely-available (for educational use) *Hot Potatoes* software, recommended for this purpose by the Primary Framework.

*Hot Potatoes* **user** (page 38) provides a format for recording the process of finding out how to use new software: including using the onscreen buttons. They could also make notes to help them to write a 'Getting started' section for a users' manual.

**Helpdesk** (page 39) should be used once the children have discovered how to use a specific section of *Hot Potatoes* (or another piece of computer software). Ask them to keep a note of any queries they have, then they could help one another to find the answers. Their notes could form the basis of a 'FAQ' (frequently asked questions) section for a users' manual or for a helpdesk operator's checklist. Ask them to edit their questions to ensure that they are expressed politely and in a form that is easily understood (ie, as briefly as possible and without ambiguity).

*Hot Potatoes* **glossary** (page 40) lists some of the technical vocabulary used in the *Hot Potatoes* software and asks the children to enter the definitions. It is useful for them to read and then write out the definitions, rather than doing this on a computer by copying and pasting, as this helps them to make sense of them and remember them. However, they could also begin their own electronic computer terms glossary (using a table in a word-processing program such as *Word*) to which the can add new words as they come across them in their ICT wor The meanings of some of the words will become apparent after they use the software but they can check these and look up the others using the Internet or printed dictionaries. Online sources might be easier to find since printed dictionaries on this quickly developing technology soon become out of date. They should check the software's own glossary. Useful websites include http://www.webopedia.com/, http://foldoc.org/.

## Recounts

> These activities develop the children's skills in devising questions to find information and making notes which could inform the writing of a recount. They learn by observing expert interviewers and reading or watching and listening to written recounts and broadcasts by expert recount-writers.

**Interview** (page 41) develops skills in devising questions to find the facts of an event in order to plan and write a recount. The children could first read some newspaper recounts about local events and notice the sources of information, especially quotes or reported speech from eye-witnesses or people affected. The children could work in groups: each group writing questions to ask another group, who deduce the answers from the picture.

**The interviewer** (page 42) helps the children to plan an interview with a visitor to the school or someone the class visits. They should prepare for the interview by reading about the topic or watching television programmes or DVDs about it and then writing notes about the facts they know. Allow them time to talk about this with their groups and to consider anything they do not know or which puzzles them.

**The best questions** (page 43) develops the children's awareness of the types of questions that elicit the most information. After carrying out an interview using their prepared questions (page 42), they can review the responses to these questions and should discover that open questions elicit more information than those that can be answered by yes or no. Ask them what was similar or different about the questions, which produced the most information, about the characteristics of the most effective questions: for example the opening words.

**Recount chronology: 1** and **2** (pages 44–45) develop the children's awareness that a recount should present events so that the order in which they took place is clear although it might not begin with the first event. It also develops their awareness of how quotations and reported speech are used.

**count features** (page 46) provides a format to help the children to identify the key features of a recount. It is based on the recount *Village Oak Mystery* (page 44) but it could be adapted for analysing other recounts. The children learn that the structure of a recount includes the use of an introduction to orientate the readers and make them want to read on and a summary to indicate what might happen as a result of the events to explain something. They also learn how quotations from eye-witnesses enliven a recount and demonstrate its reliability.

## Persuasive writing

This section develops skills in identifying how language can be used in order to persuade people to do something through appealing to their feelings, common sense, values and aspirations. The activities also focus on the techniques of persuasion: for example, rhetorical questions, sentences in the imperative mood, ambiguity, half-truth, bias and the expression of opinions as if they are facts.

**Dear Editor: 1** and **2** (pages 47–48) help the children to identify the devices used in letters to persuade readers to do something or to agree with a point of view. The children should also notice the structure of the letters: the first paragraph introduces the topic and presents the facts (albeit with bias); subsequent paragraphs present the writer's views (presented in a persuasive way and sometimes as if they are facts); and the final paragraph summarises the argument. It is useful first to ensure that the children understand the terms used: *fact, bias, sequencing, main points, comparison, opinion, appealing, values.*

**Persuasive language** (page 49) focuses on the use of powerful and sometimes emotive vocabulary in advertisements as well as devices such as half-truths, rhetorical questions and ambiguity. You will need to explain these terms, using examples, and to remind the children of their previous learning about verbs, adjectives and connectives. They could also use this chart to help them to identify these features in other advertisements.

**different bias: 1** and **2** (pages 50–51) present similar facts written from opposing points of view in order to help the children distinguish between fact and opinion and to recognise bias in writing. They should compare the connotations of words (compare *harmless tricks* with *bullying* and *blackmail, annual fun night* with *sinister practice, small gifts of goodies* with *sackfuls of sickly chocolate* and *amazing outfits* with *identities disguised*). They should also notice the contrasting adjectives used in each report: 1) fun, harmless, exciting, amazing; 2) threatened, scared, callous, disguised, evil, sickly, tooth-rotting, sinister. In the second report the children should also notice the use of contrast and comparison to suggest that what looks harmless and fun is, in fact, evil and harmful.

# Poetry

## *Poetic style*

Here the children read and respond to poems by two contrasting writers, noticing their interests, features of their style and what they can tell about the poets from their writing. Grace Nichols and Robert Louis Stevenson are featured and there are activities that can be used in connection with the work of other poets.

**Robert Louis Stevenson** (page 52) presents two poems by Robert Louis Stevenson, who was born and grew up in Scotland in the nineteenth century. He suffered from illness throughout his childhood and was often confined to bed but his nurse told him stories of far-off places that fired his imagination and made him want to travel (which he did later). The poems give some indication of Stevenson's childhood and his interest in travel. Some of the words and phrases indicate his Scottish heritage and the time he lived in: *counterpane* (a word now rarely used for a bed cover) and *kirk* (a Scottish word for a church). Draw the children's attention to the regular rhyme patterns of these poems and the descriptive language and the jogging narrative rhythm; the poet sets out to describe imagined scenes through nouns and adjectives, with verbs in the first person that express his interaction with the scenes he imagines. The children could compare the poems with anything they imagine about everyday scenes or situations.

**Grace Nichols** (page 53) presents two poems by Grace Nichols, a contemporary poet from Guyana (now living in Britain). The poems give some indication of her interests: everyday life and the power of nature, both of which she observes in detail. Some of the observations give an indication of her home country: village life that includes a donkey and a market bus, hurricanes and hibiscus. Draw the children's attention to the absence of any particular rhyme pattern in these poems: 'Sea Timeless Song' has no rhyme and 'Early Country Village Morning' has an irregular rhyme pattern (in the first verse the first two lines rhyme; in the second there is no rhyme and in the third verse the second and fourth lines rhyme). Draw attention to the rhythms of the poems: 'Early Country Village Morning' seems to gather strength as the village wakes up, whereas 'Sea Timeless Song' has the rhythm of the tide. Also note the use of onomatopoeia (*clip-clopping, yawn*) and personification (the sun yawns and pushes darkness out of her eye as if rubbing a sleepy eye on awakening). In the second verse the alliteration of the *s* sounds suggests the sound of the sea washing in and out on a shore and the repetition of *sea timeless* creates an impression of timelessness.

**Researching a poet** (page 54) helps the children to identify key aspects of a poet's style. It can be used with pages 52 and 53 or in connection with the work of other poets. Children could also write a 'style guide' for a poet, summarising that poet's style. Children in the class could research several different poets. See the Children's Poetry Archive at http://www.poetryarchive.org/childrensarchive/home.do for other ideas.

**Free verse: 1** and **2** (pages 55–56) develop the children's understanding of free verse by drawing their attention to the key features of a poem in this style. Draw their attention to the lengths of the lines and the rhythm of the poem. The lines are of varying lengths with no regular pattern and it reads like a monologue in prose, although it is set out in lines, unlike prose, which is continuous. The powerful images the poem conjures up are created through the dog metaphor. The word *dog* is not used but the children should easily recognise the metaphor from the nouns, verbs and adjectives: (nouns) *leash, head, eyes, tongue, tail, legs*; (verbs) *run, whimpered, panting, looked*; (adjectives) *frightened, confused*. Ask them how the poem makes them feel (they might already have expressed this through exclamations while reading it). Ask the children how the poem is different from their stories based on the poem. They should notice the layout and how this affects the way in which they read the poem. Invite feedback with a volunteer reading the prose passage aloud and another reading the poem.

### Classic narrative poems

This section focuses on well-known poems that tell a story. It features *The Listeners* by Walter de la Mare and includes ideas that can be used with this or with other poems.

**Is there anybody there?** and **The traveller** (pages 57–58) prepare for the introduction of the poem *The Listeners* by Walter de la Mare (page 59). The first image (page 57) provides a focus for exploring the setting and its atmosphere and predicting what might happen there before the children read the poem. The second activity (page 58) introduces the character (the traveller) and prepares the children for what happens in the poem, which presents a short episode from a story, leaving the reader with a mystery. You could also prepare a 'story bag' containing objects linked with the poem for the children to explore and discuss: a riding whip, stirrups, reins, boots, an envelope sealed with sealing wax bearing an illegible (perhaps water-smudged) name written in pen and ink, a cloth or leather pouch or bag, a picture of a horse, a horse-shoe.

**The Listeners** (page 59) presents the poem *The Listeners* by Walter de la Mare. After introducing the poem (pages 57–58), read it to the children and allow them time to read it again for themselves and talk to their groups about it. Ask them why the traveller might be knocking at the door, who might be in the house (if anyone) and why no one was there if the traveller had said he would come. Also ask them what they think might happen next. Page 60 could be used for group work at this point. Re-read the first four lines with them, highlighting the use of language to communicate the look and atmosphere of the setting. Then read the next four lines and ask the children about the contrast (the knocking on the door in the silence of the wooded setting).

**The Listeners atmosphere** (page 60) focuses on the atmosphere of the poem. This could be used alongside page 59, after the children have read the poem but before they have identified the words that create the atmosphere. Before they begin to sort these cards they could write some of their own ideas about the atmosphere of the poem and write words on other cards (provide a blank copy of the grid).

### Choral and performance

This section encourages the children to express their responses to poems they listen to. The activities help them to identify the features that make a poem good to listen to and how a poem should be read.

**Listening to poems** (page 61) provides a format to help the children to record their responses to poems they listen to. These could be on the radio, television, CD-ROMs, DVDs or the Internet but the children will not see the texts before they hear them. It is useful to prepare for this by discussing a poem they listen to and using it to demonstrate the meanings of pace, rhythm, mood, meaning and message. Otherwise use CDs or online recordings. Discuss the fact that some poetry is part of an oral tradition and that books and printing have changed the way we encounter poetry (in modern UK culture at least).

**Read it aloud** (page 62) is about how to read a poem. In this activity the children read a poem they have not listened to and discuss the best ways of reading it. They should first consider what the poet is saying and then consider different tones of voice for reading different sections of the poem. The first stanza is a warning to the woman's friends and family, spoken with the defiance of a naughty child. The second stanza continues in this vein but the third provides contrast by describing the real lifestyle of the woman and should be spoken in a 'prim and proper' way. Then the fourth stanza introduces a touch of mischief, as if the woman is about to try out some of her ideas.

**Sounds good** (page 63) presents a poem that creates an image of stillness and calm while saying that there is no time for this; it creates an image of what *could* be and as such is a good example of persuasive writing. Through contrast, it seems to say 'This is what we should be doing'. The children are asked to identify the words and phrases and the poetic devices that help to create this atmosphere: the rhyme of long vowel sounds (and their repetition) in words such as *care, stare, boughs, cows, pass, grass, light, night, glance, dance*; and alliteration of soft consonants and the slow pace they create in words such as *life, if, stand, stare, streams, stars*.

**Sounds good to me** (page 64) helps the children to record their responses to the poems they most like listening to. They identify the words and phrases whose sounds they enjoy and which create effects such as fear, excitement, stillness, humour. Children could also record themselves and others performing their favourite poems to create a class poetry anthology.

12

# Using the CD-ROM

The PC CD-ROM included with this book contains an easy-to-use software program that allows you to print out pages from the book, to view them (e.g. on an interactive whiteboard) or to customise the activities to suit the needs of your pupils.

## Getting started

It's easy to run the software. Simply insert the CD-ROM into your CD drive and the disk should autorun and launch the interface in your web browser.

If the disk does not autorun, open 'My Computer' and select the CD drive, then open the file 'start.html'.

Please note: this CD-ROM is designed for use on a PC. It will also run on most Apple Macintosh computers in Safari however, due to the differences between Mac and PC fonts, you may experience some unavoidable variations in the typography and page layouts of the activity sheets.

## The Menu screen

Four options are available to you from the main menu screen.

The first option takes you to the Activity Sheets screen, where here you can choose an activity sheet to edit or print out using Microsoft Word.

If you do not have the Microsoft Office suite, you might like to consider using OpenOffice instead. This is a multi-platform and multi-lingual office suite, and an 'open-source' project. It is compatible with all other major office suites, and the product is free to download, use and distribute. The homepage for OpenOffice on the Internet is: www.openoffice.org.)

The second option on the main menu screen opens a PDF file of the entire book using Adobe Reader (see below). This format is ideal for printing out copies of the activity sheets or for displaying them, for example on an interactive whiteboard.

The third option allows you to choose a page to edit from a text-only list of the activity sheets, as an alternative to the graphical interface on the Activity Sheets screen.

Adobe Reader is free to download and to use. If it is not already installed on your computer, the fourth link takes you to the download page on the Adobe website.

You can also navigate directly to any of the three screens at any time by using the tabs at the top.

## The Activity Sheets screen

This screen shows thumbnails of all the activity sheets in the book. Rolling the mouse over a thumbnail highlights the page number and also brings up a preview image of the page.

Click on the thumbnail to open a version of the page in Microsoft Word (or an equivalent software program, see above.) The full range of editing tools are available to you here to customise the page to suit the needs of your particular pupils. You can print out copies of the page or save a copy of your edited version onto your computer.

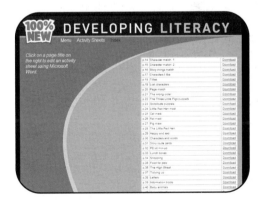

## The Index screen

This is a text-only version of the Activity Sheets screen described above. Choose an activity sheet and click on the 'download' link to open a version of the page in Microsoft Word to edit or print out.

## Technical support

If you have any questions regarding the *100% New Developing Literacy* or *Developing Mathematics* software, please email us at the address below. We will get back to you as quickly as possible.

educationalsales@acblack.com

# A Martian comes to stay

- **Read the passage.**
- **Then fill in the chart on page 15.**

It was on the second day of Peter's holiday with his grandmother that the Martian came to the cottage. There was a knock at the door and when he went to open it there was this small green person with webbed feet and eyes on the end of stumpy antennae who said, perfectly politely, "I wonder if I might bother you for the loan of a spanner?"

"Sure," said Peter. "I'll ask my gran."

Gran was in the back garden, it being a nice sunny day. Peter said, "There's a Martian at the door who'd like to borrow a spanner."

Gran looked at him over her knitting. "Is there, dear? Have a look in Grandad's toolbox, there should be one there."

Peter found the spanner and took it back to the Martian, who held out a rather oddly-constructed hand and thanked him warmly. "We've got some trouble with the gears or something and had to make an emergency landing. And now the mechanic says he left his tools back at base. I ask you! It's all a mystery to me – I'm just the steward. Anyway – thanks a lot. I'll bring it back in a minute." And he padded away up the lane. There was no one around, but then there wasn't likely to be: the cottage was a quarter of a mile from the village and hardly anyone came by except the occasional farm tractor and the odd holidaymaker who'd got lost. Peter went back into the garden.

"Should have offered him a cup of tea," said Gran. "He'll have had a fair journey, I shouldn't wonder."

"Yes," said Peter. "I didn't think of that."

In precisely three minutes' time there was another knock at the door. The Martian was there, looking distinctly agitated. He said, "They've gone."

"Who's gone?" said Peter.

"The others. The spaceship. All of them. They've taken off and left me."

Gran by now had come through from the garden. She hitched her specs up her nose and looked down at the Martian, who was about three and a half feet high. "You'd best come in," she said, "while we have a think. Gone, you say? Where was it, this thing of yours?"

From *A Martian Comes to Stay* by Penelope Livel

**Teachers' note** Read the passage with the children or give them time to read it independently. Ask them if it made them want to read the rest of the story. Ask for reasons. What did they not like? What made them want to read more? Discuss how Penelope Lively engages the reader's interest. See also page 15.

**100% New Developing Literacy Understanding and Responding to Texts: Ages 9–10** © A & C BLACK

# Stories by Penelope Lively

- Read the passage with a friend.
- Compare it with other stories by Penelope Lively.
- Write notes on the chart.

Is it an adventure, mystery, suspense story, myth, legend, historical story or science fiction?

Is it modern, nearly modern, old, ancient or in the future? Is it real-life or imaginary?

Are they ordinary everyday characters? Do they meet fantastical ones? Think about their relationships.

| Title | Type of story | Setting | Characters |
|---|---|---|---|
| A Martian comes to stay | | | |
| | | | |
| | | | |

**NOW TRY THIS!**

- Make another chart to compare themes or issues from one author's stories.  friendship   prejudice   other theme or issue

---

**Teachers' note**  Use this with page 14. Ask the children to consider the different types of story they know and in which categories this one could fit. Is it a realistic or imaginary setting? Are the characters realistic or imaginary? Compare it with other stories by Penelope Lively and note the main similarities (see suggestions for other stories in the Introduction, page 5).

**100% New Developing Literacy**
**Understanding and Responding**
**to Texts: Ages 9–10**
**© A & C BLACK**

# Anne Fine story openings

- **Read these story openings.**
- **Then fill in the spaces on page 17.**

## A Really Awful Start

When Bill Simpson woke up on Monday morning, he found he was a girl.

He was still standing staring at himself in the mirror, quite baffled, when his mother swept in.

"Why don't you wear this pretty pink dress?" she said.

"I never wear dresses," Bill burst out.

"I know," his mother said. "It's such a pity."

And, to his astonishment, before he could even begin to argue, she had dropped the dress over his head and zipped up the back.

"I'll leave you to do up the shell buttons," she said. "They're a bit fiddly and I'm late for work."

And she swept out, leaving him staring in dismay at the mirror. In it, a girl with his curly red hair and wearing a pretty pink frock with fiddly shell buttons was staring back at him in equal dismay.

From *Bill's New Frock* by Anne Fine

## Bad News Bear

I'm not a total lame-brain. Nor am I intergalactically stupid. And I don't go wimp-eyed and soggy-nosed when bad things happen to me. But I confess, as I looked round the dismal swamp that was to be my new classroom, I did feel a little bit cheesy. Oh, yes. I was one definite Bad News Bear.

"Lovely news, everyone!"

Miss Tate clapped her hands and turned to the lines of dim-bulbs staring at me over their grubby little desks.

"We have somebody new this term," she said. "Isn't that nice?" She beamed. "And here he is. He's just flown in from America and his name is Howard Chester."

"Chester Howard," I corrected her.

But she wasn't listening. She was busy craning round the room, searching for a spare desk. And I couldn't be bothered to say it again. I reckoned she was probably bright enough to pick it up in time. So I just carried my stuff over to the empty desk she was pointing towards, in the back row.

"And that's Joe Gardener beside you," Miss Tate cooed after me.

"Hi, Gardener Joe," I muttered, as I sat down.

From *How to Write Really Badly* by Anne Fine

100% New Developing Literacy
Understanding and Responding
to Texts: Ages 9–10
© A & C BLACK

# Story openings

- What is the author trying to do in the | opening | ?
- Write notes about how she does this.

Title _____    Author _____

| Set the scene | Introduce main character |
|---|---|
|  Detailed description? Recount? Dialogue? | Character as narrator? Author as narrator? Dialogue? Description? |

| Grab reader's interest | Introduce relationships |
|---|---|
| Action? Problem? Interesting point of view? Mystery? | Family? Friends? Teacher/pupils? Tension or struggle? |

**NOW TRY THIS!**

- Compare the openings of four books by the same author.
- List the similarities and differences.

achers' note  Use this with page 16 or with other stories by Anne Fine or a different author. Ask
e children how the author uses the opening: how she introduces the characters, the setting and
e story. If this sheet is used for a story by a male author change the bullet point in the
structions to *he*.

# Story sorts

- **Sort the stories into four sets.**
- **Think about the similarity between the stories in each set.**

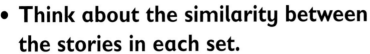

Work with a friend.

| | | |
|---|---|---|
| Persephone and the Pomegranate seeds | The Ant and the Grasshopper | Robin Hood and the Sheriff of Nottingham |
| The Lion and the Mouse | King Arthur and the Knights of the Round Table | Androcles and the Lion |
| The Three Little Pigs | King Alfred and the Burnt Cakes | King Midas (who turned everything he touched into gold) |
| The Gingerbread Man | The Hare and the Tortoise | The Story of the Glastonbury Thorn |
| Saint George and the Dragon | The Story of Rama and Sita | Goldilocks and the Three Bears |
| Jason and the Golden Fleece | The Minotaur | The Fox and the Hen |

**Teachers' note** Recap the four categories with the children before starting. Ask the children to cut out the cards and, in groups, to identify the stories they (or some of them) know. Leave out any they do not know. Ask them to sort the cards into sets and to discuss how those in each set are similar. Invite feedback.

100% New Developing Literacy
Understanding and Responding to Texts: Ages 9–10
© A & C BLACK

# Creation myths

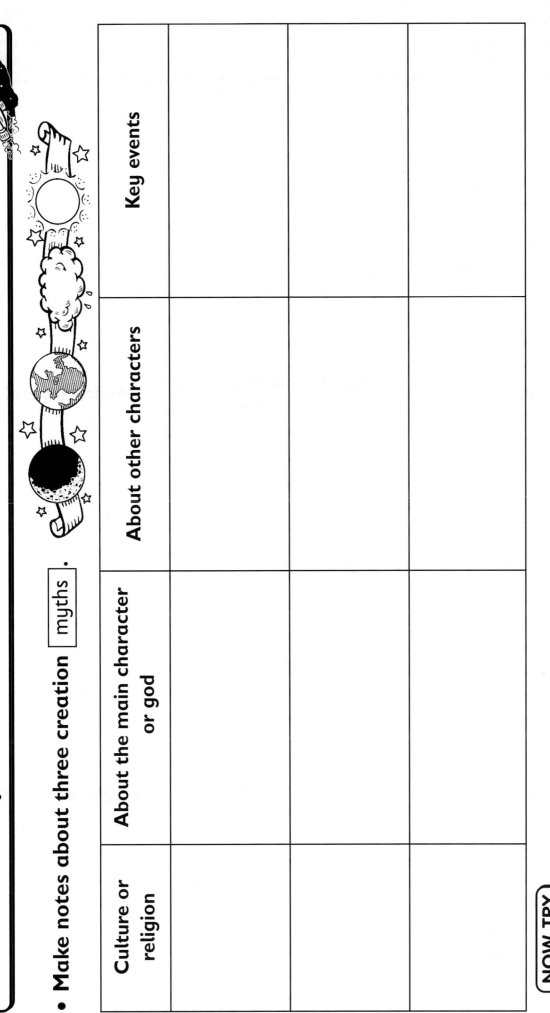

- Make notes about three creation ⬚myths⬚ .

| Culture or religion | About the main character or god | About other characters | Key events |
|---|---|---|---|
| | | | |
| | | | |
| | | | |

- List the similarities between the creation myths.

achers' note  Different groups of children could read different creation myths (see Introduction
ge 8) and make notes about the characters and key events. Before this activity you could ask
lunteers to re-tell the stories to the rest of the class (link this to religious education). Ask them to
plain why most cultures or religions have a creation myth.

100% New Developing Literacy
Understanding and Responding
to Texts: Ages 9–10
© A & C BLACK

# Fabulous fables

- ## What is the message of each | fable |?
- ## Write in the boxes.

Work with a friend.

### The ant and the grasshopper

One summer's day a grasshopper was hopping about in a field, singing. An ant passed by carrying a huge ear of corn.

"Come and have fun instead of working," said the grasshopper.

"I am collecting food for the winter," said the ant. "You should do the same."

"Why bother about winter?" said the grasshopper. "We have plenty of food." The ant went on working. When the winter came the grasshopper starved, but the ants had plenty to eat.

### The boy who cried wolf

There was once a shepherd boy who wanted some attention and excitement. One evening he rushed into the village shouting, "Wolf, wolf!" The villagers came running out to kill the wolf but they could not find it. The boy enjoyed this so much that a few days later he did it again. Again the villagers came to help. Again they found no wolf.

Not long afterwards a wolf began to attack the sheep. The boy ran to the village shouting, "Wolf, wolf!" This time no one came to help.

### The fox and the crow

A crow perched in a tree holding a piece of meat. Before long a fox came along and wanted the meat. He said, "How beautiful the crow is! If her voice were as beautiful as her looks she would be queen of the birds." The crow wanted to show that her voice was beautiful, too, and opened her beak to caw. The meat fell to the ground. The fox snatched it up, and said to the crow, "Your voice is fine, but your brains are not."

### The bundle of sticks

An old man who was dying asked his servant to bring a bundle of sticks, and he said to his eldest son, "Break it." The son strained and strained but, however hard he tried, he could not break the bundle. The other sons tried, too, but could not break it. "Untie the sticks and take one. Now, break it," said the father.

Each stick broke easily.

**Teachers' note** Ask the children what they know about fables (stories – usually very short – with a message). The best known fable-writers are Aesop (Greek, 6th century BCE) and Jean de la Fontaine (French, 17th century). After they have read the stories, invite feedback about messages, settings and characters (especially personification of animals).

**100% New Developing Literacy Understanding and Responding to Texts: Ages 9–10**
© A & C BLACK

# The legend of Gelert: 1

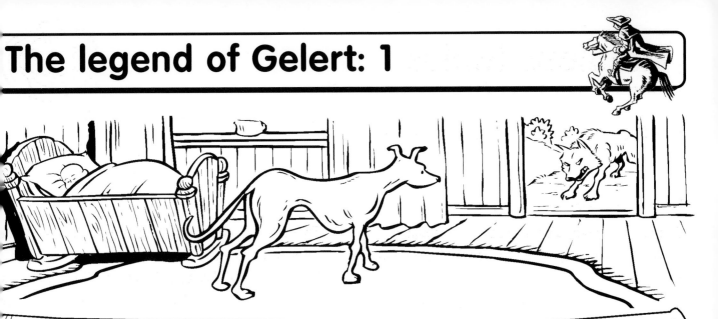

Llewellyn, prince of North Wales, loved hunting. He had hunting-houses where he and his family used to stay during his hunting trips. One of them was at the place now called Beddgelert. In those days wolves used to roam the countryside there in large packs.

On one trip, Llewellyn set off from this house with a hunting party and his hounds. This time he did not take his favourite hound, Gelert. He had a more important job for him.

His wife Joan stayed in the house with their baby son and he wanted to make sure they were safe, so he set the faithful Gelert to guard them.

It was a good hunt: they killed three or four wolves and Llewellyn rode home with the others. He thought it odd that Gelert did not run out to meet him.

"Gelert!" he called, but Gelert did not come.

He went into the house. Joan was sleeping. Then he saw Gelert.

The hound lay beside the baby's cradle. It had been overturned. There was blood everywhere. Gelert's fur was matted with blood.

"Oh, Gelert! What have you done?" cried the prince. And he ran his sword through the hound.

Gelert gave a great sad howl of pain.

Then Llewellyn heard another cry. It came from beneath the upturned cradle. He lifted the cradle, and there was the baby. Then he saw the body of a wolf. Now he knew what had happened.

"Poor Gelert!" sobbed Llewellyn and stroked his head. Gelert licked his master's hand as he died.

Llewellyn had a coffin made for Gelert and gave him a proper funeral. The faithful hound was buried in a grave marked by a stone under the weeping willow in the village that is named after him – Beddgelert ('grave of Gelert').

**eachers' note** After the children have read the story, ask them how it is similar to, and different om, a fable. Legends are not intended to give messages but this one could be interpreted in that ay ('Think before you act'). Ask them if they think it could be a true story: setting, characters and vents. Discuss how they can find out. (See also Introduction page 8.)

**100% New Developing Literacy Understanding and Responding to Texts: Ages 9–10** © A & C BLACK

# The legend of Gelert: 2

- **What can you find out about the** [ legend ] **of Gelert?**
- **Write notes on the chart.**

Use the Internet.

---

**Prince Llewellyn**

Was he a real person? _____ When did he live? _____

Where did he live? _____

What was his wife's name? _____ Did he have children? _____

---

**Beddgelert**

Is it a real place? _____ Where is it? _____

When does it date from? _____

**Give a description**

Village

_____

_____

_____

Location

_____

_____

_____

Gelert's grave _____

---

**The legend**

Are any parts true? _____

Where did it come from? _____

---

**NOW TRY THIS!**

- **Use your notes to help you to write a review of the legend.**

---

**Teachers' note** Use this with page 21. The children could use books and the Internet to help them to find out about the characters in the story, the setting and the events. Ask them how much of this legend they think is true and which parts they think were made up.

**100% New Developing Literacy Understanding and Responding to Texts: Ages 9–10**
**© A & C BLACK**

# 'Parvana's Journey'

rvana's family has been separated during the war in Afghanistan. Fearing for her safety, she left her village er her father died. In a bombed house she found a baby she calls Hassan. She came across Asif living in a ve. She stopped writing about her real experiences and began to imagine something different...

---

*Dear Shauzia*

*This morning we came to a hidden valley in the Afghan mountains, so secret that only children can find it. It's all green, except where it's blue or yellow or red, or other colours I don't even know the names of. The colours are so bright you think at first they will hurt your eyes, but they don't. It's all so restful.*

---

rvana kept writing, and as her words filled the page, she could see Green Valley ore clearly in her mind. It almost became real.

Writing to your friend again?" Asif asked from where he was sitting.

Do you want to hear it?"

Why would I want to hear what a couple of girls have to say to each other?"

You'll like this," Parvana said. "Let me read it to you."

sif didn't say yes, but he didn't say no, so Parvana read out what she had written.

---

*Green Valley is full of food. Every day we eat like we are celebrating the end of Ramadan. I just finished eating a big platter of Kabuli rice with lots of raisins and big hunks of roasted lamb buried inside it. After that I ate an orange as big as my head and three bowls of strawberry ice cream. No one in Afghanistan has ice cream anymore, except for the children of Green Valley, and we can have as much as we want. You would love it here. Maybe when you get tired of France you could come here, and this is here we could meet instead of the Eiffel Tower. Now that I've found this place, I never want to leave. We can drink the water here without boiling it, and we don't get sick. The other children tell me it's magic water. All the children here have both arms and legs. No one is blind, and no one is unhappy. Maybe Asif's leg will even grow back.*

---

rvana finished reading. She sighed deeply and put the letter down. It sounded foolish. While she was riting it, she could see everything so clearly! But now she could only think about her empty belly, sif's terrible cough and blown-off leg, and the horrible smell coming from Hassan.

om *Parvana's Journey* by Deborah Ellis

eachers' note After the children have read the passage ask them what they can tell about the ulture and place in which the story is set. Ask them how the author uses contrast to highlight the rim reality of Parvana's life and what the letter about her imagined life says about the reality. Ask em how it makes them feel. See also page 24.

100% New Developing Literacy
Understanding and Responding
to Texts: Ages 9–10
© A & C BLACK

# Language in 'Parvana's Journey'

- **Think about Parvana's real experiences and what she imagines.**
- **How does the author use language to show the difference?**
- **Write on the chart.**

*Work with a friend.*

| | Real | Imagined |
|---|---|---|
| **Person** | | |
| Adjectives | | |
| Comparisons | | |
| Strong verbs | | |

*List the adjectives.*

**NOW TRY THIS!**

- **What do the negative words in the letter tell you about Parvana's real life?**

*Look for not, no, never, none, and so on.*

**Teachers' note** Ask the children to re-read the passage on page 23 and to notice the way in which the author chooses words to create and effect. They should notice contrasting adjectives and the comparisons and the strong verbs (see Introduction page 8 for examples).

**24**

100% New Developing Literacy
Understanding and Responding
to Texts: Ages 9–10
© A & C BLACK

# Characters and culture

Talk to a friend about the picture.
Write what you would do if you came across this place.
Write what different story characters might do.

Write notes.

| I would | Parvana from *Parvana's Journey* |
|---|---|
|  |  |

Character _____

Story _____

Character _____

Story _____

**NOW TRY THIS!**

- **Explain how each person's culture affects what he or she does.**

**achers' note** You could copy the page and display it (or just the picture) on an interactive hiteboard. Discuss what it shows, where this might be and what has happened there. Ask the ildren to imagine they could step into the picture. How would they feel? Why? What would ey do?

100% New Developing Literacy
Understanding and Responding
to Texts: Ages 9–10
© A & C BLACK

# Culture and actions

- **How did the** culture **affect a character's actions?**
- **Make notes on the note pad.**

Title _____

Author _____

Culture _____

Character _____

| Action | How culture affected it |
|--------|------------------------|
| _____ | _____ |
| _____ | _____ |
| _____ | _____ |
| _____ | _____ |
| _____ | _____ |
| _____ | _____ |
| _____ | _____ |
| _____ | _____ |
| _____ | _____ |

**NOW TRY THIS!**

- **Explain how each character's earlier experiences affect what he or she does.**

**Teachers' note** Use this with *Parvana's Journey* or another story set in a different culture. Ask the children if the culture affected what the characters did: for example, earlier in *Parvana's Journey* we read that she had disguised herself as a boy for some time because life was safer for boys.

**100% New Developing Literacy Understanding and Responding to Texts: Ages 9–10**
© A & C BLACK

# An older novel

itle _____

uthor _____ Year _____

## nd of chapter summaries

| Chapter | Main events | My questions | My predictions |
|---|---|---|---|
| 1 | | | |
| 2 | | | |
| 3 | | | |
| 4 | | | |
| 5 | | | |

**NOW TRY THIS!**

• **Describe any surprises you had while reading the novel.**

Oh!

achers' note  Use this page to help the children to write a reading journal of an older novel that read in serial form. At the end of each chapter arrange a plenary session during which the ildren summarise what has happened so far, any queries they have and what they think might appen next.

**100% New Developing Literacy
Understanding and Responding
to Texts: Ages 9–10**
© A & C BLACK

# Different dialogue

- **Would you talk to your friends using this type of language?**
- **Underline the parts you would not use.**
- **Number them.**
- **On the notepad, write the numbers and write what you would say instead.**

*William and his friends (the "Outlaws") are talking about the local fair.*

"①<u>Gosh</u>! It seems years an' years since the las' time they came," said William.

"I got a coconut as near as near," said Ginger, "I bet I get one quite nex' time."

"If there is a nex' time," said Douglas. "P'raps they've lost the map an' forgot the way."

The Outlaws walked on down the road for some time in silence. Gradually the gloom cleared from William's countenance.

"Tell you what!" he said. "Let's do somethin' excitin' ourselves to make up."

"What?" said Ginger.

"How excitin'?" said Douglas a little apprehensively.

"We'd never do anythin' as excitin' as the Wall of Death," said Henry.

"We won't try an' do the things they do in fairs," said William. "We'll do somethin' quite diff'rent.  Somethin' we've never done before."

"What?" said Ginger again.

William was silent for a few moments; then, with a burst of inspiration: "We'll have a Secret Society."

"Gosh, yes," said Ginger. "That's a jolly good idea."

*From William and the Tramp by Richmal Crompton*

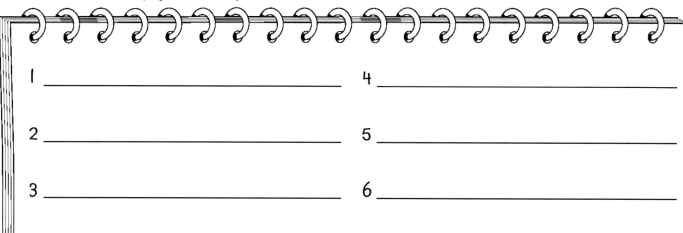

1 _____    4 _____

2 _____    5 _____

3 _____    6 _____

**Teachers' note** After the children have read the passage, ask them whether they think this story was written recently, a few years ago, when their parents or grandparents were young, or long ago in history. Discuss how they can tell from the language, and underline any words or phrases they would not use. Explain the meanings of any unfamiliar ones.

100% New Developing Literacy
Understanding and Responding
to Texts: Ages 9–10
© A & C BLACK

# Formal or informal

After Mary's parents died in India she was sent to live with an uncle in England. She wants some gardening tools and seeds. Martha is the housemaid and Dickon is her brother.

How  formal  do you think the language is?
Underline examples of older English.
Rewrite the letter as a girl might write to her brother nowadays.

*My Dear Dickon,*

*This comes hoping to find you well as it leaves me at present. Miss Mary has plenty of money and will you go to Thwaite and buy her some flower seeds and a set of garden tools to make a flower-bed. Pick the prettiest ones and easy to grow because she has never done it before and lived in India which is different. Give my love to mother and every one of you. Miss Mary is going to tell me a lot more so that on my next day out you can hear about elephants and camels and gentlemen going hunting lions and tigers.*

> *Your loving sister,*
> *Martha Phoebe Sowerby*

From *The Secret Garden* by Frances Hodgson Burnett

_____

_____

_____

_____

_____

_____

_____

_____

_____

_____

**Teachers' note** Remind the children of their previous work on letters including formal and informal language. After they have read the letter, ask them if anything surprised them and focus on examples of formal language, including the language Martha uses to refer to Mary as well as for opening and signing-off of the letter.

**100% New Developing Literacy
Understanding and Responding
to Texts: Ages 9–10**
© A & C BLACK

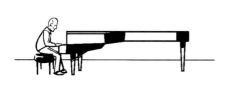

**Teachers' note** The children should first have watched, listened to and responded to the animated film *The Piano* by Aidan Gibbons (see Introduction page 9). The children could use the pictures to help them tell the story, or they could put them in order of appearance in the film and then in chronological order to draw out that the story is told through flashbacks. See also pages 31–33.

**100% New Developing Literacy**
**Understanding and Responding**
**to Texts: Ages 9–10**
**© A & C BLACK**

# 'The Piano': mood cards

| | | |
|---|---|---|
| anguished | calm | carefree |
| distressing | dreamlike | gentle |
| grim | happy | light-hearted |
| loving | melancholy | mournful |
| moving | mysterious | peaceful |
| quiet | romantic | sad |
| sorrowful | tender | touching |
| tranquil | warm | wistful |
| exciting | thrilling | horrific |

**Teachers' note** The children should first have carried out the activity on page 30. Working in groups the children could cut out the cards and split them into sets: those that described the mood of the film and those that do not. They can then take the first set and begin to arrange them on a zone of relevance grid. Ask them to give evidence for each word they choose. See also pages 32–33.

**100% New Developing Literacy
Understanding and Responding
to Texts: Ages 9–10
© A & C BLACK**

**31**

# 'The Piano': a life in a tune

- **Write the piano player's answers.**

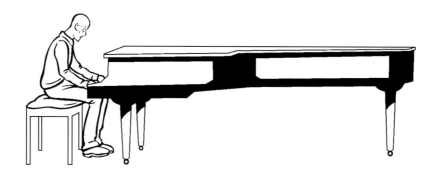

**1 What is your very earliest memory?**

_____

_____

_____

**2 Who were your family?**

_____

_____

**3 What are your happiest memories?**

_____

_____

**4 What are your saddest memories?**

_____

_____

**NOW TRY THIS!**

- **Make a time-line.**
- **Write some events from the piano player's life on it.**

**Teachers' note** The children should first have carried out the activity on pages 30–31. Replay the film and think about the questions it answers (and any it leaves unanswered) about the man's life. After writing the questions the children could replay it to look for answers, supporting them with evidence from the film. See also page 33.

100% New Developing Literacy
Understanding and Responding
to Texts: Ages 9–10
© A & C BLACK

**Write what the characters are thinking and saying.**

**NOW TRY THIS!**

• **Write a longer dialogue for one of the scenes.**

achers' note  The children should first have carried out the activity on pages 30–32. Replay the
m to look more closely at the scenes shown here. The children could enact them with a partner
alone, if easier), speaking the words or just thinking them. Remind them of the mood of the
n (see page 31) and consider any words which better communicate this mood.

**100% New Developing Literacy
Understanding and Responding
to Texts: Ages 9–10**
© A & C BLACK

**33**

# Script match

- **Match the** scripts **to the television programme types.**
- **Explain your answers.**

Think about person, tense, type of sentence and style of language.

**1** After a cold start (between 1 and 2 degrees Celsius) the northeast of England will have a mainly sunny day.

**2** A goal from Didier Drogba towards the end of extra time made the final score one nil – giving Chelsea victory over Manchester United in the first FA Cup final at the new Wembley stadium.

**3** Have you ever wondered why some face creams are so expensive? Don't be fooled by fancy packaging…

**4** Escomb is one of the most complete small Anglo-Saxon churches in England. It is not known exactly when the church was built but it is thought to be before AD700.

**5** Fire-fighters rescued two children from a burning house in York after their mother called 999 at 5 am today.

**6** Welcome to the show, Tony. Now, tell us about your invention. What does it do?

**8** Your two minutes start now – What is the largest artificial lake in Europe?

**9** Under the dark water of the lake is a forest of green plants. Among them live countless fish…

**7** Carragher heads the ball to Terry. Is he going to take a shot? Yes! What a save from Helton! So it's still England nil, Brazil nil, after 60 minutes.

**10** Now you can afford that new sofa – nothing to pay until August next year.

**11** Traffic came to a standstill on the A1 north of Berwick today after a lorry shed its load.

| Programme type | Script | How I can tell |
|---|---|---|
| News | | |
| Advertisement | | |
| Sports report | | |
| Sports commentary | | |
| Documentary | | |
| Quiz show | | |
| Chat show | | |
| Weather forecast | | |

**Teachers' note** What do the children watch or listen to that has a script? Draw out that most non-fiction radio and television programmes, as well as plays, are based on scripts. Do they know any programmes which cannot be scripted beforehand? Look for clues to help match the scripts to the programmes: subjectmatter, person, tense, tone and connectives used.

**100% New Developing Literacy Understanding and Respondin to Texts: Ages 9–10 © A & C BLACK**

# In the script

Watch some ⟨ scripted ⟩ television extracts.
Listen to some scripted radio extracts.
Make notes about them on the chart.

To entertain, inform, instruct or persuade.

Advertisement, chat show, documentary, news, quiz show, cooking or gardening programme, sports commentary or report, weather forecast.

| Title | Type | Purpose |
|-------|------|---------|
|  |  |  |
|  |  |  |
|  |  |  |
|  |  |  |
|  |  |  |
|  |  |  |
|  |  |  |
|  |  |  |

**NOW TRY THIS!**

- **Choose one extract.**
- **Explain how it is good for its purpose.**

achers' note  Prepare for this activity by recording extracts from some different types of radio
d television programmes (live or from the broadcasting companies' websites). After the children
ve identified the type of programme from the list provided, ask them to consider what each type
programme is for. Why do people watch or listen to it?

**100% New Developing Literacy
Understanding and Responding
to Texts: Ages 9–10
© A & C BLACK**

# Presentation

- Make notes about the features of some [information] radio and television programmes.

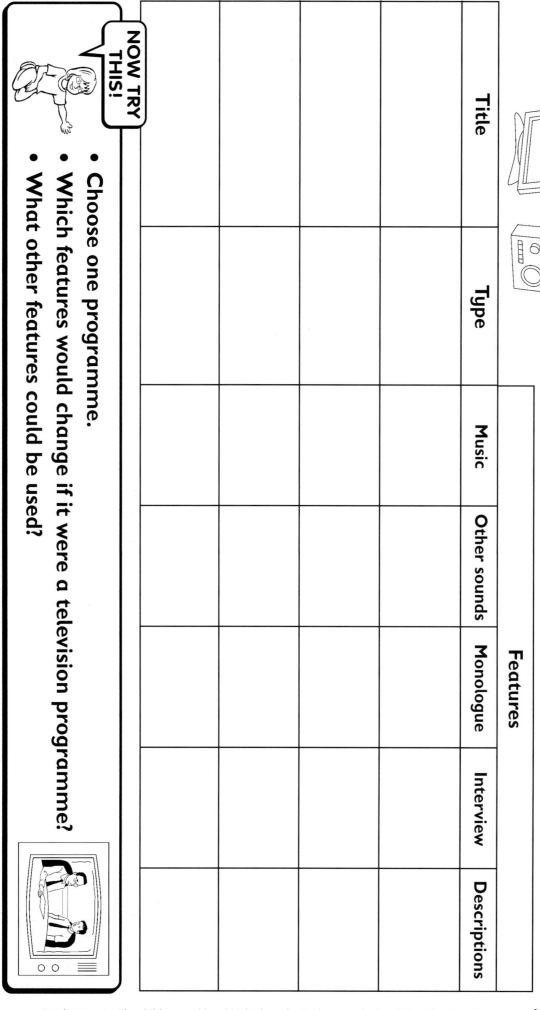

| Title | Type | Features | | | | | |
|---|---|---|---|---|---|---|---|
| | | Music | Other sounds | Monologue | Interview | Descriptions |
| | | | | | | |
| | | | | | | |
| | | | | | | |
| | | | | | | |

**NOW TRY THIS!**

- Choose one programme.
- Which features would change if it were a television programme?
- What other features could be used?

Teachers' note  The children could revisit the broadcasts they watched or listened to for the previous activity. This time, ask them to notice the different features of the programmes and the main differences between radio and television. They might notice how radio programmes help the listener to visualise objects or scenes.

100% New Developing Literacy
Understanding and Respondin[g]
to Texts: Ages 9–10
© A & C BLACK

# Evaluate a broadcast

- **Evaluate a television or radio broadcast.**

Title _____  Type _____  Purpose _____

- **Colour the thermometers to show how good the features were.**

| 1 | poor | 2 | good | 3 | brilliant |

- **Write examples in the boxes.**

Music

| 3 | | |
| 2 | | |
| 1 | | |

Spoken words

| 3 | | |
| 2 | | |
| 1 | | |

Song

| 3 | | |
| 2 | | |
| 1 | | |

Other sounds

| 3 | | |
| 2 | | |
| 1 | | |

Camera angle

| 3 | | |
| 2 | | |
| 1 | | |

**NOW TRY THIS!**

- **Use your notes to help you to write a review of the broadcast.**

**Teachers' note** This could be based on some of the television broadcasts that were used for pages 35 and 36. The children could revisit five of these and consider what was good about them and what was not so good: for example, did the music help to set the scene or would a voice-over or silence have been better? Did they want a closer look at something in the picture?

100% New Developing Literacy
Understanding and Responding
to Texts: Ages 9–10
© A & C BLACK

# 'Hot Potatoes' user

The 'potato' we used was ✔

| JCloze | ☐ | | JMatch | ☐ | | JQuiz | ☐ |
|--------|---|---|--------|---|---|-------|---|
| JCross | ☐ | | JMix | ☐ | | | |

To find out how to use it, this is what we did.

These helped: ✔

☐ → ☐ → ☐ → ☐

What helped you the most? _____

What help do you still need? _____

Where will you look for this help? _____

**NOW TRY THIS!**

• What should a newcomer to *Hot Potatoes* do first?

**Teachers' note** Use this with the computer software *Hot Potatoes* (see Introduction page 10). During ICT lessons let each group explore a different section of the software without giving them any instructions. One member of the group could act as observer – making notes about what they did in order to find out how to use it.

**100% New Developing Literacy**
**Understanding and Responding**
**to Texts: Ages 9–10**
© A & C BLACK

# Helpdesk

Write [ questions ] about using a new computer program.
Find the answers.
Write them in the [ answer ] bubbles.

Think about what you need to know and in what order.

**Questions**

**Answers**

**NOW TRY THIS!**

• **List the most important points about getting started.**

**eachers' note** Use this with the computer software *Hot Potatoes*. Ask the children to make notes bout the important questions that were raised while they were exploring the software and the nswers they found. They could enact a 'helpdesk' scene, using appropriate language. Encourage em to share their ideas about how to use the software.

**100% New Developing Literacy Understanding and Responding to Texts: Ages 9–10**
**© A & C BLACK**

**39**

# 'Hot Potatoes' glossary

- **Write the meanings of the words used in the program *Hot Potatoes*.**

 Use the Help file.

 Use a dictionary.

 Use the Internet.

| Word | Definition |
|---|---|
| auto response | |
| clone | |
| feedback | |
| gapping | |
| hybrid | |
| interface | |
| multiple choice | |
| reset | |

**NOW TRY THIS!**

- **Make a glossary of icons for the potato you used.**

**Teachers' note** Ask the children to make a note of any words they come across that were new to them or to others. Ask them how they found the meanings and how they could help others to understand new words connected with the software. They could also create a table in *Word* or other word-processing software that will sort the list into alphabetical order.

100% New Developing Literacy
Understanding and Responding
to Texts: Ages 9–10
© A & C BLACK

# Interview

Write four questions to find out what happened.
Write the eye-witnesses' answers.

**NOW TRY THIS!**

• Use the interview to help you to plan a recount.
• Use details from the picture.

**Teachers' note** Ask the children to imagine they are reporters who have arrived at the scene to find out what has happened. They could think up questions to ask the eye-witnesses on the scene. Encourage them to use what they can find out from their observations to help them to pose questions.

**100% New Developing Literacy
Understanding and Responding
to Texts: Ages 9–10**
© A & C BLACK

# The interviewer

- **Plan an** | interview | **with someone who has seen an interesting event.**

Work in a group.

The event _____

The eyewitness _____

| What we know | What we want to know | Our questions |
|---|---|---|
| | | |

**NOW TRY THIS!**

- **Interview the eyewitness.**
- **Record the answers.**

You could write notes or use an audio-recorder.

**Teachers' note** Use this page to help the children to plan an interview with someone who has witnessed an interesting or important event (or who lived through an interesting period of history). Through discussion in their groups they can then consider what they want to know, and write questions that will help.

**100% New Developing Literacy Understanding and Responding to Texts: Ages 9–10 © A & C BLACK**

# The best questions

- Evaluate an [interview].
- Which questions gained the most information?

| The best questions | |
|---|---|
| Question | Answer |
| | |
| | |
| | |

| The worst questions | |
|---|---|
| Question | Answer |
| | |
| | |
| | |

Notice the opening words of the questions.

**NOW TRY THIS!**

- How are the best questions similar?
  How are the worst questions similar?

---

**Teachers' note** After carrying out or listening to an interview the children could consider what they found out through the questions that were asked. Were there any one-word answers? Were some of these just yes or no? Ask them how the questions could be changed to draw out more information. You could introduce the terms *open* and *closed* questions.

## Village Oak Mystery

'Old Tom' last summer.

Residents of Oakfield woke up this morning to find a huge gap where an ancient oak, known locally as 'Old Tom', used to stand.

During the night there had been gentle breezes but no strong winds and even if the tree had blown down it would surely be lying on its side on the green, but there was no trace of the tree. No roots remained in the ground, there were no stray twigs or leaves on the green and, said local residents, the old oak had been laden with acorns the day before but not a single acorn could now be seen on the green.

Oakfield resident Maria Greenstreet, 38, said, "I went out at midnight to look for my cat. He was stuck in the oak tree. I had to climb up and lift him out," adding that she had been wearing her nightdress and slippers.

But Cary Itoff, 25, said he thought he heard a heavy vehicle driving into the village and stopping. He and his band had been practising in his garage until the early hours of the morning. The others had left at about 4 am.

The *Daily Blab* managed to contact Gary Basher, 23, the band's drummer. "Oh, yes," he said. "At about 5 am I saw a huge gang of people sweeping the green by torchlight and piling rubbish into bags. There was a long articulated lorry parked right on the green. I didn't notice if the tree was still standing, but there were a lot of squirrels rushing about looking very agitated."

Lisa Lott, 57, said she was returning from a late shift at 5.30 am when she saw a large blue articulated lorry leaving Oakfield in the direction of Elmfield. She managed to read the sign on the side of the lorry as she passed it: 'George Oakley and Sons, timber suppliers'.

Police are investigating the matter. Inspector Justin Time said, "We have had reports of a large red lorry leaving Oakfield in the opposite direction to Elmfield at 5.20, with no sign on it," he said, "so people should not jump to the conclusion that Oakley's have stolen the tree." He added that a 57-year-old woman was helping the police with their enquiries.

Meanwhile Oakfield residents mourn the loss of their ancient oak. "There is an old saying that when Old Tom goes, Oakfield goes," said Jeremiah Sage, 107.

**Teachers' note** Remind the children of the structure of a recount: introduction, events recounted in a way that shows chorological order, summary paragraph. Reading in pairs, underline features such as *past tense verbs, time connectives* and *quotations*. Identify examples of direct speech (using speech bubbles) and reported speech (using expressions such as *said that*).

**100% New Developing Literacy Understanding and Responding to Texts: Ages 9–10**
**© A & C BLACK**

# Recount chronology: 2

**Write summaries of the** | key events | **in the** | recount |.
**Cut out the boxes and glue them on the timeline in the order in which they happened.**

Oak tree on green laden with acorns.

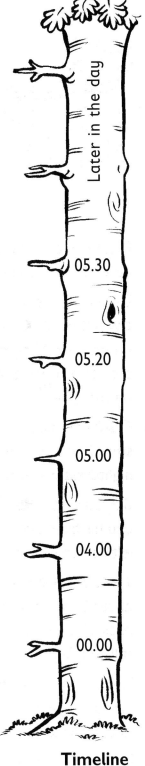

Later in the day

05.30

05.20

05.00

04.00

00.00

**Timeline**

**NOW TRY THIS!**

- Use your notes to help you to write the recount in the order in which it happened.
- Compare this with the original.

**Teachers' note** Use this with page 44. The children could first cut the recount into separate paragraphs and arrange them in the order in which the events happened. Discuss why it was not written strictly in this order and how the writer indicated the order in which everything happened.

**100% New Developing Literacy Understanding and Responding to Texts: Ages 9–10**
© A & C BLACK

# Recount features

- **Give examples of the features of** | recounts | **from**
*Village Oak Mystery.*

| Feature | Examples |
|---|---|
| Heading | |
| Introduction | |
| Past tense verbs | |
| Time connectives | |
| Quotations | |
| Reported speech | |
| Summary | |
| Indication of what might happen next | |

**NOW TRY THIS!**

- **How is a recount different from an explanation?**
- **Plan an explanation of *Village Oak Mystery.***

---

**Teachers' note** Use this with page 44. Ask the children to reread the recount and to look for the features listed on the chart. Ask them about the purpose of a recount (to tell a story in a way that shows the order in which events happened and how they were connected to one another).

**100% New Developing Literacy
Understanding and Responding
to Texts: Ages 9–10**
© A & C BLACK

# Dear Editor: 1

## Read these letters to a local newspaper.

**1**

Dear Editor

Summerton was a lovely village but over the years traffic has increased so much that the High Street is part of a major trunk road.

Huge lorries thunder through, shaking the very foundations of the old Tudor buildings and covering them with layers of oily dust. They pour out polluting gases that fill our lungs.

A bypass might take small slices off a few fields but the gain to the village will be immeasurable.

Yours faithfully

Anita Place, High Street

**2**

Dear Editor

Snobbs, the only department store in town, has big signs on its doors: "No unaccompanied children". This is an example of discrimination. It suggests that children are thieves, vandals or trouble-makers. Reading the columns of your newspapers, I find that more than 90% of the crimes in this town are committed by adults. It would be fairer if Snobbs' signs read "No unaccompanied adults".

I urge other children and young people to write to Snobbs to complain.

Yours faithfully

June O'Hoo (age 10), Market Street

**3**

Dear Editor

Our region offers perfect locations for wind turbines: open moorland at altitudes of up to 700 metres, largely uninhabited. Yet there are always strong objections to wind turbines. The objectors say they will spoil the landscape, create noise and damage wildlife. Would they prefer a silent but deadly form of damage in the form of nuclear power stations? That is what we will face if the country cannot generate enough electricity from renewables such as wind power.

Does anyone ever object to living close to a traditional windmill? I do not think so. We cannot go back in time. We have to build efficient, modern wind turbines.

Wind farms have their own beauty in the right setting. Nuclear power stations are always ugly.

Think about it before you protest.

Yours faithfully,

Lester Gripe, Top Heath

**4**

Dear Editor

I used to play football in the park but now I am not allowed to for two main reasons: children have been attacked and robbed there and the grass is fouled by dogs.

We all pay tax to the council. We deserve better than this. We need someone to supervise the park all the time it is open. This would keep park users safe. It would also help to stop vandalism and therefore save the council money. It would also help to catch dog-owners who do not clean up after their pets. They could enforce fines and this, too, would bring in money for the council. So the cost of employing a park supervisor would probably be more than paid for by the savings on repairs and the money from fines.

It makes no sense not to employ a supervisor.

Yours faithfully

Justin Goal (age 9), Match Green

**Teachers' note** After the children have read the letters, ask them about their purpose. Do they inform, ask for something, ask for information, explain, thank, congratulate or persuade? Ask the children how they can tell that these were written to persuade: focus on persuasive language, appeals to people's values and emotions, suggestions that any other view would be wrong and so on.

**100% New Developing Literacy Understanding and Responding to Texts: Ages 9–10 © A & C BLACK**

# Dear Editor: 2

- **How do the letter-writers** persuade **their audience?**
- **Give examples.**

| Persuasive technique | Letter | Examples |
|---|---|---|
| Presenting the facts in a biased way | | |
| Sequencing the main points | | |
| Comparison — What is compared with what? | | |
| Presenting opinions as if they are facts | | |
| Appealing to common sense | | |
| Appealing to audience — Who are the audience? What might they value? | | |

**Teachers' note** Ask the children to reread the letters on page 47 and to look for examples of persuasive language: bias, sequencing, comparisons, opinions given as facts, appeals to 'common sense' as if there is only one sensible view and appeals to the audience's known values.

**100% New Developing Literacy
Understanding and Responding
to Texts: Ages 9–10**
© A & C BLACK

# Persuasive language

Look for examples of | persuasive | language.
List them on the chart.

## Silver wheels

Probably the world's fastest heelies.

Do you want to impress your friends?

Here's your chance.

Take up our amazing offer.

Come and try a pair **FREE**.

Surely there could be no better offer.

Naturally, you'll find cheaper heelies but common sense will tell you that you only get what you pay for. If you want the best you'll want to pay that little bit more for what must be the perfect heelies.

• Specially designed by a top scientist so that there's almost **no friction**.

• Friction is what slows you down. Remove the friction and you'll move closer to the **speed of light**.

• The less friction the **faster** you go.

| Powerful verbs | |
|---|---|
| Powerful adjectives | |
| Persuasive connectives | |
| Rhetorical questions | |
| Ambiguity | |
| Half-truths | |

**NOW TRY THIS!**

• **Rewrite the text without any persuasive language.**

Just write the facts.

**ichers' note** The children should read the advertisement and identify how the writer tries to luence the audience. They could underline the key words and phrases. Ask them to notice how s advertisement implies ideas without actually stating false facts.

**100% New Developing Literacy**
**Understanding and Responding**
**to Texts: Ages 9–10**
**© A & C BLACK**

# A different bias: 1

• **Read these reports. Which report approves of 'trick or treat'?**

**(1) Halloween fun**

It's time for the annual fun night for children, when even the little ones are allowed to stay up late and call at neighbours' houses to play harmless tricks on them or accept small gifts of goodies. It's a night when neighbours can get to know one another.

'Trick or treat' becomes more popular every year and shops stock ever more exciting costumes and masks as well as bags of goodies for everyone. Everyone can enjoy the amazing outfits of witches, skeletons, ghosts and ghouls and even robots and monsters. Everyone can have a feast.

Halloween livens up the dark days of late autumn.

**(2) Dangerous tricks and unhealthy treats**

Tonight thousands of children are planning to go around bullying old people into giving them money or sweets. Bullying? Yes. Any behaviour that makes someone feel threatened or scared is bullying. They may call it harmless fun. That's what many bullies say about their callous behaviour.

'Trick or treat' is not an old tradition to keep up, but a modern import from the USA. It encourages children to misbehave with their identities disguised, to dress up specially to scare old people and to forget all they know about good behaviour.

They go around after dark, facing possible danger from traffic, and blackmail folk into giving them treats which they would be better off without: sackfuls of sickly chocolate and sweets oozing with tooth-rotting sugar.

There are many good reasons for banning this sinister practice.

**100% New Developing Literacy
Understanding and Respondin
to Texts: Ages 9–10
© A & C BLACK**

# A different bias: 2

**Compare the two reports about Halloween.
How can you tell that the writers are** | biased | **?
List the evidence.**

---

**Report 1**

Writer's point of view: _____

Examples of bias:

Adjectives _____

Nouns _____

Verbs _____

Opinions stated _____

as facts _____

---

**Report 2**

Writer's point of view: _____

Examples of bias:

Adjectives _____

Nouns _____

Verbs _____

Opinions stated _____

as facts _____

---

**NOW TRY THIS!**

- **Write an unbiased report about Halloween.**

---

**Teachers' note** Ask the children to reread the two reports on page 50 and to look for examples of language that present the facts in ways that express different opinions. Remind them of what they have learned about the connotations of words and point out how words can be used to appeal to the reader's emotions.

100% New Developing Literacy
Understanding and Responding
to Texts: Ages 9–10
© A & C BLACK

# Robert Louis Stevenson

- **Read the poems aloud with a friend.**
- **Underline the parts you like the best.**
- **Write notes in the margins about why you like them.**
- **Link these to the correct line in the poem.**

## The land of counterpane*

When I was sick and lay a-bed,
I had two pillows at my head,
And all my toys beside me lay,
To keep me happy all the day.

And sometimes for an hour or so
I watched my leaden soldiers go,
With different uniforms and drills,
Among the bed-clothes, through the hills;

And sometimes sent my ships in fleets
All up and down among the sheets;
Or brought my trees and houses out,
And planted cities all about.

I was the giant great and still
That sits upon the pillow-hill,
And sees before him, dale and plain,
The pleasant land of counterpane.

\* a bed cover

## Block city

What are you able to build with your blocks?
Castles and palaces, temples and docks.
Rain may keep raining, and others go roam,
But I can be happy and building at home.

Let the sofa be mountains, the carpet be sea,
There I'll establish a city for me:
A kirk and a mill and a palace beside,
And a harbour as well where my vessels may ride.

Great is the palace with pillar and wall,
A sort of a tower on the top of it all,
And steps coming down in an orderly way
To where my toy vessels lie safe in the bay.

This one is sailing and that one is moored:
Hark to the song of the sailors aboard!
And see, on the steps of my palace, the kings
Coming and going with presents and things!

Now I have done with it, down let it go!
All in a moment the town is laid low.
Block upon block lying scattered and free,
What is there left of my town by the sea?

Yet as I saw it, I see it again,
The kirk and the palace, the ships and the men,
And as long as I live and where'er I may be,
I'll always remember my town by the sea.

**Teachers' note** Give the children time to read and enjoy the poems. They should read them (or listen to them being read) aloud to become aware of their rhythm and rhyme pattern. Discuss from whose point of view the poems are written and ask whether this reveals anything about the poet.

100% New Developing Literacy
Understanding and Responding
to Texts: Ages 9–10
© A & C BLACK

# Grace Nichols

- Read the poems with a friend.
- Underline the parts you like the best.
- Write notes in the margins about why you like them.
- Link these to the correct line in the poem.

## Early country village morning

Cocks crowing
Hens knowing
later they will cluck
their laying song

Houses stirring
a donkey clip-clopping
the first market bus
comes juggling along

Soon the sun will give a big yawn
and open her eye
pushing the last bit of darkness
out of the sky

## Sea timeless song

Hurricane come
and hurricane go
but sea... sea timeless
sea *timeless*
sea *timeless*
sea *timeless*
sea *timeless*

Hibiscus bloom
then dry-wither so
but sea... sea timeless
sea *timeless*
sea *timeless*
sea *timeless*
sea *timeless*

Tourist come
and tourist go
but sea... sea timeless
sea *timeless*
sea *timeless*
sea *timeless*
sea *timeless*

Think about the subject, theme, form, rhyme pattern and rhythm.

**NOW TRY THIS!**

- **Compare these with the two poems by Robert Louis Stevenson.**

**Teachers' note** The children should read the poems (or listen to them being read) aloud to help become aware of the rhythm. Ask them how the poet uses language to create the image and feel of a real scene: for example, powerful verbs, nouns chosen for impact, personification and repetition, but no regular rhyme pattern.

**100% New Developing Literacy
Understanding and Responding
to Texts: Ages 9–10**
© A & C BLACK

# Researching a poet

Poet's name _____  Year of birth _____  Nationality _____

| Poem | Subject | Themes | Rhyme pattern | Language features: alliteration, simile, metaphor, comparison | Rhythm and pace |
|------|---------|--------|---------------|----------------------------------------------------------------|-----------------|
|      |         |        |               |                                                                |                 |
|      |         |        |               |                                                                |                 |
|      |         |        |               |                                                                |                 |
|      |         |        |               |                                                                |                 |

**NOW TRY THIS!**

- What do the poems tell you about the poet's background, interests and views?
- Write a report about the poet.

**Teachers' note** The children could begin by researching Robert Louis Stevenson and Grace Nichols. Ask them what they can infer from the poems about each writer. What do the scenes they describe and the words they use tell us about the writers – for example, their culture, aspects of their lives, their interests or way of looking at the world.

100% New Developing Literacy
Understanding and Responding
to Texts: Ages 9–10
© A & C BLACK

# Free verse: 1

## Read the poem aloud with a friend.
## Draw the scenes it makes you imagine.

### Taking my pen for a walk

Tonight I took the leash off my pen.
At first it was frightened,
looked up at me with confused eyes, tongue panting.
Then I said, "Go on, run away,"
and pushed its head.
Still it wasn't sure what I wanted;
it whimpered with its tail between its legs
So I yelled, "You're free, why don't you run –
you stupid pen, you should be glad,
now get out of my sight."
It took a few steps.
I stamped my foot and threw a stone.
Suddenly, it realised what I was saying
and began to run furiously away from me.

Julie O'Callaghan

Think about how to show the metaphor.

**1**

**2**

**3**

**4**

**5**

Teachers' note  Ask the children if this is a prose passage or a poem. How they can tell? Then give them a copy of the page and ask them if they can tell more easily now. Ask how it is like prose and draw out that it tells a story. Invite the children to describe the scenes each part makes them imagine.

100% New Developing Literacy
Understanding and Responding
to Texts: Ages 9–10
© A & C BLACK

# Free verse: 2

- **Use your drawings to help you to write the story of the poem.**

Do not look at the poem. Cover it up. Use your own words.

_____

_____

_____

_____

_____

_____

_____

_____

_____

_____

- **Read your story aloud.**
- **Listen to your group's stories.**
- **Compare them with the poem.**
- **What makes the poem poetic?**

Work in a group.

Think about how the poem creates an image and how it makes you feel.

_____

_____

_____

_____

_____

_____

Think about how it does these.

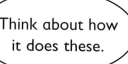

**Teachers' note** Ask the children to reread the poem on page 55. Ask how it makes them feel at different points. Cut out their numbered drawings from page 55 and use them to tell the story of the poem. Does this re-telling have the same effect? Why not? Draw out the effect of the powerful imagery through personification.

**100% New Developing Literacy Understanding and Responding to Texts: Ages 9–10**
© A & C BLACK

# Is there anybody there?

**Teachers' note**  Use this activity to introduce the classic narrative poem *The Listeners* by Walter de la Mare (page 59). Explore the setting. What can they see? What time of the day is it? What might they hear in this setting and what might it fell like to step into it? Ask them what might happen there. Who might come into the setting, and from where?

100% New Developing Literacy
Understanding and Responding
to Texts: Ages 9–10
© A & C BLACK

# The traveller

**Teachers' note** The children should first have carried out the activity on page 57. Now introduce the central character in the poem (see also page 59). Remind the children of the setting and ask them who this might be. Why is he knocking on the door? Introduce some language used in the poem to describe the arrival of the traveller.

**100% New Developing Literacy Understanding and Responding to Texts: Ages 9–10** © A & C BLACK

# 'The Listeners'

**Underline the words that are important in creating the atmosphere of the poem. On the side write notes about the** atmosphere **.
Act the scene with a friend.**

> Look for features such as rhyme, alliteration, onomatopoeia and lengths of lines.

### The Listeners

"Is there anybody there?" said the Traveller,
 Knocking on the moonlit door;
And his horse in the silence champed the grasses
 Of the forest's ferny floor:
And a bird flew up out of the turret,
 Above the Traveller's head:
And he smote upon the door a second time;
 "Is there anybody there?" he said.
But no one descended to the Traveller;
 No head from the leaf-fringed sill
Leaned over and looked into his grey eyes,
 Where he stood perplexed and still.
But only a host of phantom listeners
 That dwelt in the lone house then
Stood listening in the quiet of the moonlight
 To that voice from the world of men:
Stood thronging the faint moonbeams on the dark stair,
 That goes down to the empty hall,
Hearkening in an air stirred and shaken
 By the lonely Traveller's call.
And he felt in his heart their strangeness,
 Their stillness answering his cry,
While his horse moved, cropping the dark turf,
 'Neath the starred and leafy sky;
For he suddenly smote on the door, even
 Louder, and lifted his head –
"Tell them I came, and no one answered,
 That I kept my word," he said.
Never the least stir made the listeners,
 Though every word he spake
Fell echoing through the shadowiness of the still house
 From the one man left awake:
Ay, they heard his foot upon the stirrup,
 And the sound of iron on stone,
And how the silence surged softly backward,
 When the plunging hoofs were gone.

Walter de la Mare

**Teachers' note** You could provide a 'story bag' containing objects for the children to explore before they read the poem (see Introduction page 12). They could read it for themselves, to enjoy , before you read it aloud with them to explore the use of language.

**100% New Developing Literacy
Understanding and Responding
to Texts: Ages 9–10**
© A & C BLACK

# 'The Listeners' atmosphere

**Read *The Listeners* on page 59.**

- **Which of these cards describe the poem's atmosphere best?**

| | | |
|---|---|---|
| blustery | calm | dismal |
| echoing | eerie | foreboding |
| ghostly | grim | haunted |
| hushed | light-hearted | menacing |
| noiseless | mysterious | peaceful |
| quiet | romantic | silent |
| sinister | soundless | still |
| threatening | tranquil | uneasy |

**Teachers' note** The children should first have carried out the activity on pages 57–59. Ask the children to sort the cards according to how well they describe the atmosphere of the poem. Ask them to look for evidence in the poem to support their choices.

**100% New Developing Literacy
Understanding and Responding
to Texts: Ages 9–10**
© A & C BLACK

# Listening to poems

- Use this page to record your responses to poems you listen to.

| Title | Poet | Rhythm – and changes | Pace – and changes | Mood – and changes | Message or meaning |
|-------|------|----------------------|--------------------|--------------------|--------------------|
|       |      |                      |                    |                    |                    |
|       |      |                      |                    |                    |                    |
|       |      |                      |                    |                    |                    |
|       |      |                      |                    |                    |                    |

**NOW TRY THIS!**

- Write your ideas about what makes a poem good to read aloud.

**Teachers' note** Ask the children what difference it makes to hear a poem rather than read it to themselves. Focus on the way in which this can bring out rhyme, rhythm and other features that help to communicate meaning.

100% New Developing Literacy
**Understanding and Responding
to Texts: Ages 9–10**
© A & C BLACK

# Read it aloud

- **Plan how to read the poem aloud.**
- **Practise with a friend.**

Each verse should be read differently. Think about tone of voice.

I shall – so there!

I'll do as I like!

Tut, tut! Fancy doing that.

Just you wait!

Ha! Ha!

Very nice.

### Warning

When I am an old woman I shall wear purple
With a red hat which doesn't go, and doesn't suit me,
And I shall spend my pension on brandy and summer gloves
And satin sandals, and say we've no money for butter.
I shall sit down on the pavement when I'm tired
And gobble up samples in shops and press alarm bells
And run my stick along the public railings
And make up for the sobriety of my youth.
I shall go out in my slippers in the rain
And pick the flowers in other people's gardens
And learn to spit.

You can wear terrible shirts and grow more fat
And eat three pounds of sausages at a go
Or only bread and pickle for a week
And hoard pens and pencils and beermats and things in boxes.

But now we must have clothes that keep us dry
And pay our rent and not swear in the street
And set a good example for the children.
We will have friends to dinner and read the papers.

But maybe I ought to practise a little now?
So people who know me are not too shocked and surprised
When suddenly I am old and start to wear purple.

Jenny Joseph

**NOW TRY THIS!**

- **Describe the changes from one verse to another.**

**Teachers' note** Use this page to help the children to read a poem aloud in a way that brings out its humour. Point out the title and ask who is warning whom. What is she warning about? Discuss different warning tones: for example, threatening or menacing, light-hearted and 'just watch me'.

**100% New Developing Literacy Understanding and Responding to Texts: Ages 9–10 © A & C BLACK**

# Sounds good

- **Read the poem aloud.**
- **What makes it sound good?**
- **Underline the effective words.**
- **Write notes about what makes these parts sound good.**
- **Link them to the right place in the poem.**

### Leisure

What is this life if, full of care,
We have no time to stand and stare.

No time to stand beneath the boughs
And stare as long as sheep or cows.

No time to see, when woods we pass,
Where squirrels hide their nuts in grass.

No time to see, in broad daylight,
Streams full of stars like skies at night.

No time to turn at Beauty's glance,
And watch her feet, how they can dance.

No time to wait till her mouth can
Enrich that smile her eyes began.

A poor life this if, full of care,
We have no time to stand and stare.

W H Davies

_____

_____

_____

_____

_____

_____

_____

_____

_____

_____

_____

_____

_____

_____

**NOW TRY THIS!**

- **What is the message of this poem?**
- **Describe how the poet's choice of words helps to communicate this message.**

eachers' note  Let the children read this poem to themselves and give them time to respond to it
efore asking them about its message and meaning, atmosphere and mood and the words and
hrases that communicate these. Ask them how they think it should be read.

100% New Developing Literacy
Understanding and Responding
to Texts: Ages 9–10
© A & C BLACK

# Sounds good to me

- **What are your favourite poems to listen to?**
- **Write the lines you like to hear.**
- **Note what you like about them.**

Think about the effects of... rhythm, rhyme, alliteration, onomatopoeia, powerful verbs and adjectives.

| Title | Poet | Line | What I like about the sound |
|---|---|---|---|
|  |  |  |  |
|  |  |  |  |
|  |  |  |  |

**NOW TRY THIS!**

- Describe the effects of these lines of poetry.

**Teachers' note**  After listening to several poems read aloud, the children could choose their four favourites to listen to. Ask them to think about what makes them good to listen to, particularly how effects such as rhyme and rhythm help to communicate meaning and atmosphere.

**100% New Developing Literacy Understanding and Responding to Texts: Ages 9–10**
© A & C BLACK